BRITTLE FRACTURE IN STEEL STRUCTURES

Brittle Fracture
in Steel Structures

Editor:

G.M. Boyd, O.B.E., F.R.I.N.A.,
M.I. Struct. E., F.Weld.I.

CRC PRESS

A DIVISION OF
THE CHEMICAL RUBBER CO.
CLEVELAND, OHIO

INTERNATIONAL SCIENTIFIC SERIES

ENGLAND: BUTTERWORTH & CO. (PUBLISHERS) LTD.
              LONDON: 88 Kingsway, W.C.2
AUSTRALIA: BUTTERWORTH & CO. (AUSTRALIA) LTD.
              SYDNEY: 20 Loftus Street
              MELBOURNE: 343 Little Collins Street
              BRISBANE: 240 Queen Street
CANADA: BUTTERWORTH & CO. (CANADA) LTD.
              TORONTO: 14 Curity Avenue, 374
NEW ZEALAND: BUTTERWORTH & CO. (NEW ZEALAND) LTD.
              WELLINGTON: 49/51 Ballance Street
              AUCKLAND: 35 High Street
SOUTH AFRICA: BUTTERWORTH & CO. (SOUTH AFRICA) LTD.
              DURBAN: 33/35 Beach Grove

ISBN   0 408 70042 4

Published by Butterworth & Co (Publishers)
for the Navy Department Advisory Committee on Structural Steel

Printed in Great Britain by Hazell Watson & Viney Ltd, Aylesbury, Bucks

CONTENTS

PREFACE

The Navy Department Advisory Committee on Structural Steels (see list of membership, page xii) is a continuation of the Admiralty Ship Welding Committee which was set up in 1943 to study the brittle failures which at that time were occurring in welded ships. In the early years, much of the work was concerned with improvements in welding procedures and equipment used in shipbuilding, but in the course of the work it became clear that the incidence of brittle fracture was as much affected by the properties of the steel as by welding factors, and that improvements were needed in the notch toughness of standard shipbuilding and structural steels in general use at that time. In recent years the Committee has continued to study brittle fracture phenomena and is at present the main British repository of expert knowledge in this subject. The Committee has felt that the salient aspects of the problem, and methods for dealing with it, should be more widely available to practising engineers, and has therefore compiled this book.

The book is mainly concerned with mild steel structures, fabricated by welding from rolled steel plates and sections, and does not cover forgings, castings, or special steels. These, and also cases involving extremes of temperature, severe impact loading, or in which the consequences of a fracture would be very serious, require special investigation, which is not attempted in this book.

Brittle fracture is characterised by sudden failure of a structure or component at a level of loading well below that at which the general stress reaches a significant proportion of the yield point of the material, and usually below the nominal design working stress. Most such fractures initiate from some form of notch giving rise to a stress concentration. If the local yield at the tip of the notch is insufficient to spread the stress over a larger area a brittle fracture may be initiated. Once started, the brittle fracture will run at high speed until total failure occurs or it runs into conditions favourable to an arrest. The risk of occurrence of brittle fracture depends on the notch ductility* of the steel under the particular stress, temperature and other environmental factors prevailing at the time.

The first Chapter of the book gives the historical background and summarises numerous case histories of brittle fractures that have occurred in service, with a review of the lessons learned from them. Chapters 2, 3 and 4 describe the nature of the phenomenon and the factors which influence its incidence, as well as the various methods of testing that have been developed

---

* The term 'notch ductility' is used, rather loosely, in this book to denote a property of metals, indicating their resistance to brittle fracture. The property cannot be precisely defined in the present state of knowledge—Ed.

to determine the notch ductilities of different steels. Chapter 6 reviews the main methods in current use for assessing the degree of notch ductility needed for different applications, while Chapter 7 gives practical procedures, recommended by the Navy Department Advisory Committee on Structural Steels, for assessing the suitability of different steels for particular applications. Some 'Golden Rules' are given in the Appendix which designers, engineers and managements are enjoined to observe in order to minimise the risk of catastrophic failure of the structures for which they are responsible.

It is emphasised that no generally agreed analytical method has so far been developed which would give absolute confidence in the suitability of a particular steel for a particular application. Rapid strides are, however, being made in the field of fracture mechanics and there are good prospects that the existing methods may ultimately be extended to apply to the structural steels in common use. The first of the recommended procedures in Chapter 7 is therefore an arbitrary one, based on judgement and experience over a wide range of industrial applications. The second method is based directly on a particular method of testing, but although it is being increasingly adopted for statically loaded structures, it does not cover all conditions which may occur.

The book has been compiled by a Committee representing many shades of opinion and concerned with many differing applications. It cannot therefore reflect exactly the views of all the members, but rather a concensus of these views.

It is intended to review the book as further knowledge is gained and any comments to assist in this objective would be welcomed. Comments should be forwarded to the Publishers: Messrs Butterworth & Co. (Publishers) Ltd.

The NDACSS feels that the collective guidance which they are able to give in this book at this time on the selection of materials, although not very definitive, is of sufficient value to justify publication. They recognise, however, that for many important applications, designers will feel the need to consult expert opinion on their particular problems before committing themselves to a choice of steel.

Note on Units

Although the Committee fully supports the policy of changing to the Metric System, and in particular to the internationally accepted 'S.I.' units, it has been decided to retain, in this book, the more familiar units as quoted from the original sources cited, with the most commonly used metric equivalents given in parentheses. To facilitate conversion further, a set of ready-reference conversion scales is given on page ix.

Attention is invited to the 'Golden Rules' given in the Appendix (p. 115), which designers, engineers, and managements are enjoined to observe in order to minimise the risk of catastrophic failure of the structures for which they are responsible.

CONVERSION OF UNITS

Scales for ready reference (approximate)

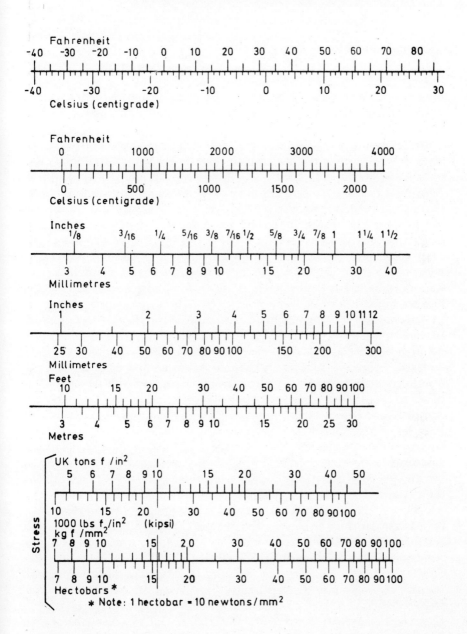

Fahrenheit
-40 -30 -20 -10 0 10 20 30 40 50 60 70 80

-40 -30 -20 -10 0 10 20 30
Celsius (centigrade)

Fahrenheit
0 1000 2000 3000 4000

0 500 1000 1500 2000
Celsius (centigrade)

Inches
1/8 3/16 1/4 5/16 3/8 7/16 1/2 5/8 3/4 7/8 1 1 1/4 1 1/2

3 4 5 6 7 8 9 10 15 20 30 40
Millimetres

Inches
1 2 3 4 5 6 7 8 9 10 11 12

25 30 40 50 60 70 80 90 100 150 200 300
Millimetres

Feet
10 15 20 30 40 50 60 70 80 90 100

3 4 5 6 7 8 9 10 15 20 25 30
Metres

Stress

UK tons f /in²
5 6 7 8 9 10 15 20 30 40 50

10 15 20 30 40 50 60 70 80 90 100
1000 lbs f₂/in² (kipsi)
kg f /mm²
7 8 9 10 15 20 30 40 50 60 70 80 90 100

7 8 9 10 15 20 30 40 50 60 70 80 90 100
Hectobars *

* Note: 1 hectobar = 10 newtons/mm²

Energy

Ft.lbs f
5 6 7 8 9 10 15 20 30 40 50 60 70 80 90 100

kg f.m 1 1·5 2 3 4 5 6 7 8 9 10 15

Joules 10 15 20 30 40 50 60 70 80 90 100

BRIT. FRAC

INTRODUCTION

In this book the emphasis is directed to the prevention of brittle fracture in structures fabricated from mild and low alloy steel operating at normal ambient temperatures.

Brittle fracture may be defined as a form of fracture that occurs suddenly under a load which is not sufficient to result in general yielding across the whole of the fractured section, especially at low temperatures and usually in consequence of a stress concentration. The problem of preventing brittle fracture has been brought into prominence by the following train of events.

Until a few years before the second world war the almost universal way of fabricating steel structures was by riveting, but by 1939 welding had made considerable progress and was gaining acceptance in steelwork construction both on land and in ships. This development became vitally important for the war effort, as it was the extensive adoption of welding that enabled ship-builders in the United States to produce both dry cargo ships and tankers, for the emergency, at an unprecedented rate. Early in the war some serious fractures which could not be explained in the light of then existing knowledge occurred in some of the welded merchant vessels. These fractures when they occurred, happened suddenly without warning at low nominal stresses, revealing a state of brittleness not ordinarily associated with the behaviour of so ductile a material as ship steel. Immediate steps were taken by the American and British Governments, and by maritime agencies individually, to cope with the problem.

In the United States the Navy and the Coast Guard set up a Board of Investigation 'to enquire into the design and methods of construction of welded steel merchant vessels'. Under its direction data was collected regarding a total of 4 694 such ships built by the Maritime Commission, more than one-fifth of which had suffered fractures of varying severity, and this data served as material for very extensive researches.[1] In the United Kingdom the Admiralty Ship Welding Committee was formed, on which not only the Admiralty, now the Ministry of Defence (Navy Department), but also Lloyd's Register of Shipping and other interested parties, including several research organisations, were represented.[2] Specimens of steel removed from fractured ships as well as production plates from the shipyards were sent to Cambridge University Engineering Department and to other laboratories for examination and test.[3] Close liaison was maintained between the authorities concerned in the two countries and it is of interest that the investigations conducted by the separate American and British groups along similar lines have led to results and conclusions which agree in almost every respect.

In 1945 a Conference on the topic of Brittle Fracture in Mild Steel Plates was held at Cambridge under the joint auspices of the British Iron and Steel Research Association and the Admiralty Ship Welding Committee.[4] This conference had very valuable results in directing attention to the most urgent aspects of the problem at that time and to the fields in which investigation was most needed. In 1959 a further conference was arranged by the Admiralty (now Navy Department) Advisory Committee on Structural Steel and was supported by a still wider range of interested British organisations. This covered experience of fractures in land structures such as bridges, storage tanks, pressure vessels, penstocks and pipelines, gas cylinders and turbo-generators.[5] Many other conferences on the subject have been held in the USA and other countries.

Considerable progress has been made towards a better understanding of the nature, causes and prevention of brittle fracture—a phenomenon not confined to modern welded structures (for cases of it are found to have been reported eighty years ago), but the risk of which has become more conspicuous following the wider application of welding to steelwork of all kinds. The most important factor influencing this type of failure has been shown to lie in the properties of the materials used. In particular, it is now clear that steel which is satisfactory for riveted construction may be unsuitable when fabricated by welding.

The object of this book is, therefore, to provide designers, engineers and managements with guidance on the choice of steel, detail design and workmanship for welded structures, based on experience and on the results of research. In order to do this effectively it will be necessary to explain in some detail the phenomena and problems involved. The book is addressed primarily to designers who are, or should be, concerned with specifying the material, but it also contains information and guidance of interest to all concerned with the safety of steel structures. It gives principles of wide applicability and does not attempt detailed consideration of specialised fields of application.

References

1. *The design and methods of construction of welded steel merchant vessels: Final report of a Board of Investigation convened by order of the Secretary of the Navy,* US Government Printing Office, Washington (1947)
2. AYRE, SIR AMOS L., and BOYD, G. M., The work of the Admiralty Ship Welding Committee. *Trans. Royal Inst. Naval Architects* (1946)
3. TIPPER, C. F., *The Brittle Fracture Story,* Cambridge University Press (1962)
4. 'Brittle Fracture in Mild Steel Plates', *British Iron & Steel Research Assoc.* (1945) (also in *Engineering,* **164** (1947) and **165** (1948)
5. *Brittle Fracture in Steel,* Admiralty Advisory Committee on Structural Steel, Report P.3, HMSO (1962)

NAVY DEPARTMENT ADVISORY COMMITTEE ON STRUCTURAL STEEL

Membership of the Committee (as at Dec. 1969)

W. G. Perry, Esq., C.Eng., M.R.I.N.A., R.C.N.C. (Chairman)	Deputy Director of Naval Construction A Ship Department, Ministry of Defence
R. G. Baker, M.A., Ph.D., F.I.M., F.Weld.I.	The Welding Institute
D. Birchon, Esq., B.Sc., F.I.M., C.Eng., F.I.Mech.E., M.I.Mar.E.	Admiralty Materials Laboratory, Ministry of Defence
G. M. Boyd, Esq., O.B.E., M.R.I.N.A., M.I.Struct.E., F.Weld.I.	Formerly of Lloyd's Register of Shipping
P. R. Christopher, Esq., B.Sc., M.I.Mech.E., A.M.R.I.N.A.	Naval Construction Research Establishment, Ministry of Defence
H. C. Cotton, Esq., C.Eng., M.I.Prod.E., F.Weld.I.	British Petroleum Co Ltd
C. L. M. Cottrell, Esq., Ph.D., M.Sc., F.I.M., M.Weld.I.	Fighting Vehicles Research and Development Establishment, Ministry of Defence
W. E. Duckworth, Esq., M.A., Ph.D., F.I.M., F.I.S.	Fulmer Research Institute
N. E. Frost, Esq., B.Sc.(Eng.), C.Eng., M.I.Mec.E.	National Engineering Laboratory
S. W. Hollingum, Esq., F.I.M.	Royal Armament Research Development Establishment, Ministry of Defence
L. M. T. Hopkins, Esq., Ph.D., A.R.S.M., F.I.M.	Ministry of Technology
K. J. Irvine, Esq., Ph.D., B.Sc.	British Steel Corporation, Midland Group
H. Lackenby, Esq., M.Sc., M.R.I.N.A.	British Shipbuilding Research Association
I. M. MacKenzie, Esq., B.Sc., F.I.M.	British Steel Corporation, Scottish & North West Group
M. J. May, B.Met., Ph.D.	BISRA Inter Group Laboratories of British Steel Corporation
J. F. Mercer, Esq., F.I.M.	B.O.C. Murex, Ltd
R. W. Nichols, Esq., B.Met., F.I.M., F.Weld.I.	Reactor Materials Laboratory, UKAEA
Professor J. Nutting, M.A., Sc.D., Ph.D., F.I.M.	University of Leeds

D. Oldridge, C.Eng., A.M.R.I.N.A., D.A.E., M.Weld.I. — Ship Department, Ministry of Defence

Professor N. J. Petch, B.Sc., Ph.D., D.Met., F.I.M. — University of Newcastle-upon-Tyne

J. H. Rendall, Esq., B.Sc., A.R.S.M., F.I.M. — National Physical Laboratory

A. G. Senior, Esq., M.Sc., M.I.C.E., A.M.I.Struct.E., M.A.S.C.E., M.Weld.I., A.M.O.R.S. — W. S. Atkins & Partners

G. P. Smedley, Esq., B.Eng., B.Met., C.Eng., M.I.Mech.E., F.I.M. — Lloyd's Register of Shipping

Professor E. Smith, B.Sc., Ph.D., F.I.M. — University of Manchester

J. W. Strawson, Esq. — Bataafse Internationale Petroleum Mij

C. E. Turner, Esq., Ph.D., B.Sc.(Eng.), F.I.Mech.E. — Imperial College of Science & Technology

Professor A. A. Wells, B.Sc.(Eng.), Ph.D. — The Queen's University, Belfast

J. G. Whitman, Esq., M.Eng., Ph.D., M.I.C.E., M.W.I. — Military Engineering Experimental Establishment, Ministry of Defence

Secretary
L. Wortley, Esq., M.Met., F.I.M. — Ship Department, Ministry of Defence

Liaison Officers
Captain K. N. Ayers, U.S.C.G. — Commander, Coast Guard Activities, Europe

Commander J. R. Eshman, U.S.N. — U.S. Navy Technical Liaison Officer

CHAPTER 1

EXAMPLES OF BRITTLE FRACTURE IN SERVICE, AND THE LESSONS LEARNED FROM THEM

The object of this chapter is to present illustrative examples, taken from various branches of engineering, of serious brittle fractures that have occurred in service or in the course of testing for acceptance, and the lessons learned from them. These will be described here only in sufficient detail for their scale and the attendant circumstances to be appreciated when further reference is made to them in later chapters. It must be remarked here, however, that were it possible to calculate the risk statistically for all forms of structure, as has in fact been attempted for ships and oil tanks, this risk would be found to be fairly small. Moreover, many of the recorded fractures have been less catastrophic than those here chosen for illustration.

1.1. SHIPS

One of the earliest and most complete analyses of ship failures from brittle fractures, accompanied by conclusions drawn from their assessment, is contained in the report[1] of the Board of Investigation set up by the United States Navy as already mentioned in the Introduction. This gives many diagrams, sketches and photographs illustrating the factors that contributed to the early ship failures, the susceptibility to fracture of different designs and details, and the effectiveness of some preventive structural alterations. The report, however, is dated 1947 and it concerns only ships built in the United States under the wartime emergency shipbuilding programme of the Maritime Commission, omitting 'war casualties, collisions, groundings and other abnormal casualties, unless a particularly interesting structural failure resulted indirectly from the other damaging influence'.

In the Board's opinion the most general cause of the failures in these welded ships was 'notch sensitivity' of the steel; the American specification existing at the time not being selective enough to exclude such steels.

Although even at the height of the trouble most of the fractures described were not serious, the worst cases included 24 ships which sustained a complete fracture of the strength deck and one with a complete fracture of the bottom. Four of the eight ships lost broke in two, and four others broke in two but

Fig. 1.1. *Aerial view of failure of* S.S. Esso Manhattan *taken from one of two blimps convoying vessel*

were not lost. A photograph of a broken tanker, the 'Esso Manhattan', is reproduced in Fig. 1.1 and typical reports by US Coast Guard inspectors are reproduced in Figs. 1.2 and 1.3. Since that time, the Board concluded, 'The serious epidemic of fractures in the steel structure of welded merchant vessels has been curbed through the combined effect of the corrective measures taken on the structure of the ships during construction and after completion, improvements in new design and improved construction practices in the shipyards'.[1]

In the United Kingdom, the Admiralty Ship Welding Committee made a special study of the problem and issued several interim reports (published by HMSO) which in their findings agreed closely with the American conclusions. A later study of the problem in ships built elsewhere than in the United States gave extensive data on actual fractures[2] and reviewed the considerations leading to revision of the requirements for the steel to be used in ship construction.[3]

The only ship built in Britain since the war which broke in two was the oil tanker 'World Concord'. This was a 32 000 ton deadweight ship which broke in two during a gale in the Irish Sea, when about two years old, in November, 1954. Afterwards a co-operative technical investigation revealed that the break occurred nearly amidships, and ran approximately in line with a transverse bulkhead, at the ends of the longitudinals which were interrupted at the bulkhead (continuity being provided by brackets). The fracture had started in the bottom and travelled across it, then up both sides of the ship and across the deck. It was not continuous but consisted of a number of separate consecutive fractures which joined together in the same transverse plane of the ship. The sea at the time had been rough, with waves estimated 15–20 ft (4·5–6 m) high. The steel conformed to the specifications then in force but these did not include notch ductility requirements and most of the plates in the way of the fracture were found in fact to be notch brittle under the operating conditions. The sea temperature was 51°F (10·5° C).

The incidence of fractures in ships is a difficult matter to deal with statistically, owing to the uncertainties in assigning relative importance to fractures

REPORT OF STRUCTURAL FAILURE OF INSPECTED VESSEL
UNITED STATES COAST GUARD
#AVCG-275.

This report includes all
available information up to:
1 Apr., 1944 (Date)

DESCRIPTION OF VESSEL

NAME	OFFICIAL NO.	TYPE (Dry Cargo, Passenger, etc.)	H.C. DESIGN
SCHENECTADY	242620	Tank Vessel	T2-SE-A1
BUILDER		BUILDER'S HULL NO.	DATE COMPLETED
Kaiser Co., Inc., Portland, Oregon		1	31 Dec., '43
OWNER		OPERATOR	
War Shipping Administration		Deconhill Shipping Company	

EXTENT OF WELDING

		Hull all welded					
Yes	SIDE SHELL SEAMS	No inner bottom				Yes	DECK SEAMS
Yes	SIDE SHELL BUTTS	Yes	BOTTOM SEAMS	-	INNER BOTTOM SEAMS	Yes	DECK BUTTS
Yes	FRAMES TO SIDE SHELL	Yes	BOTTOM BUTTS	-	INNER BOTTOM BUTTS	Yes	BEAMS TO DECK
Yes	BULKHEADS	Yes	FLOORS TO SHELL	-	FLOORS TO INNER BOTTOM	Yes	DECK TO SHELL

CIRCUMSTANCES SURROUNDING FAILURE
(Attach all available details of ship's loading)

DATE OF FAILURE	TIME	SHIP'S LOCATION		
16 Jan., 1943	2230 PWT	Tied up at fitting out pier, Swan Island		
SHIP'S SPEED	COURSE		DRAFT FWD.	DRAFT AFT
0	-		6'-4"	17'-0"
SEA CONDITION	WEATHER	DIRECTION OF WAVES WITH RESPECT TO SHIP		
Still Water	Clear	No waves		
WIND FORCE	WIND DIRECTION	AIR TEMPERATURE	WATER TEMPERATURE	
Light	East wind	26° F	40°F	

DESCRIPTION OF FAILURE
(Include sketch of fracture showing starting point and relative location of welds and other structural features)

APPARENT STARTING POINT

The fracture started at the juncture of the fashion plate at the aft starboard corner of the bridge superstructure and the sheer strake.

GENERAL HISTORY AND DESCRIPTION OF FAILURE, INCLUDING KNOWN CONTRIBUTORY FACTORS:

Without warning and with a report which was heard for at least a mile, the deck and sides of the vessel fractured just aft of the bridge superstructure. The fracture extended almost instantaneously to the turn of the bilge port and starboard. The deck side shell, longitudinal bulkheads and bottom girders fractured. Only the bottom plating held. The vessel jack-knifed and the center portion rose so that no water entered the hull. The bow and stern settled into the silt of the river bottom. Sounding taken around the vessel eliminated the alleged possibility of the vessel having grounded amidships to a drop in water level.
Bending moment in still water = 184,000 Ft. x Tons   Hog amidships.
Stress in crown of deck = 9900 Lbs./in.^{2} Tension.

CLASSIFICATION OF FAILURE
Broke in two

DISPOSITION OF VESSEL
(Repaired, lost, etc.)

Vessel repaired and put in service.	
SIGNED (Name and Title)	DISTRICT

701292—47—3

Fig. 1.2. *Copy of report of structural failure of* S.S. Schenectady

in different locations. Thus, a 4-ft fracture in an internal bulkhead may actually be less important than a 4-in crack in a sheerstrake or bilge. Moreover, the great diversity in size and types of ships makes it difficult to set the numbers of fractures against a truly representative background of numbers of ships at risk. Though several statistical investigations have been published, these are not always comparable, being based on different criteria.

To put the matter in perspective it may be noted that the annual losses of

REPORT OF STRUCTURAL FAILURE OF INSPECTED VESSEL
UNITED STATES COAST GUARD
NAVCG-2752

This report includes all available information up to:

DESCRIPTION OF VESSEL　　1 Apr., 1944 (Date)

NAME	OFFICIAL NO.	TYPE (Dry Cargo, Passenger, etc.)	R.C. DESIGN
ESSO MANHATTAN	242157	Tank Vessel	T2-SE-A1
BUILDER		BUILDER'S HULL NO.	DATE COMPLETED
Sun Shipbuilding & Drydock Company		267	22 Aug.,'42
OWNER		OPERATOR	
Standard Oil Co. of New Jersey		Standard Oil Co. of New Jersey	

EXTENT OF WELDING

Hull all welded
No inner bottom

Yes SIDE SHELL SEAMS						Yes DECK SEAMS	
Yes SIDE SHELL BUTTS	Yes BOTTOM SEAMS		- INNER BOTTOM SEAMS			Yes DECK BUTTS	
Yes FRAMES TO SIDE SHELL	Yes BOTTOM BUTTS		- INNER BOTTOM BUTTS			Yes BEAMS TO DECK	
Yes BULKHEADS	Yes FLOORS TO SHELL		- FLOORS TO INNER BOTTOM			Yes DECK TO SHELL	

CIRCUMSTANCES SURROUNDING FAILURE
attach all available details of ship's loading

DATE OF FAILURE	TIME	SHIP'S LOCATION 40 fathoms of water		
29 March, 1943	1205 EST	3/4 mile inshore buoy 3, Ambrose Channel, N.Y.		
SHIP'S SPEED	COURSE		DRAFT FWD.	DRAFT AFT
14 knots	121° true		12'-1"	18'-7"
SEA CONDITION	WEATHER	DIRECTION OF WAVES WITH RESPECT TO SHIP		
Slight ground swell	Clear	On port bow		
WIND FORCE	WIND DIRECTION	AIR TEMPERATURE		WATER TEMPERATURE
Force 2	Northeast	30° to 40°		Not known

DESCRIPTION OF FAILURE
(Include sketch of fracture showing starting point and relative location of welds and other structural features)

APPARENT STARTING POINT

The fracture started in a butt weld between plates A-9 and A-10 at the crown of the deck.

GENERAL HISTORY AND DESCRIPTION OF FAILURE INCLUDING KNOWN CONTRIBUTORY FACTORS:

With a sound described variously as a thump, thud, bang, crash, or explosion, the fracture ran across the deck in way of #6 tank, and down both sides, progressing to the bilge port and starboard. The vessel jack-knifed and the bow dug under an oncoming wave. The crew abandoned in the boats and were picked up by the USCG KIMBALL. The bottom fractured later and the two portions drifted apart. The butt weld in which the crack started contained oxide, slag and porous areas.
Bending moment in still water = 225,800 Ft. x Tons.　Hog amidships.
Stress in crown of deck = 12,200 Lbs./in.^{2} Tension.

CLASSIFICATION OF FAILURE
Broke in two

DISPOSITION OF VESSEL
(Repaired lost etc.)

Repaired on drydock at Todd Erie Basin and returned to service.

SIGNED (Name and Title)	DISTRICT

Fig. 1.3. *Copy of report of structural failure of* S.S. Esso Manhattan

ships from all causes throughout the world during the past twenty years or so have fluctuated around approximately 0·3% of the tonnage, or 0·6% of the numbers, of ships at risk. The losses through ships breaking in two form a very much smaller proportion, and not all of these were due to brittle fracture.

For the fifteen years 1949–1963 the figures for ships broken in two due to causes other than fire, explosion, collision and grounding were as shown in Tables 1.1 and 1.2.

Table 1.1

Period 1949–1963 inclusive	Tankers	Dry Cargo	Total
Average number in commission*	2 431	8 404	10 835
Aggregate years of service*	36 467	126 070	162 537
Number broken in two	15	5	20
Incidence per 100 ship-years service	0·041	0·004	0·012
Risk of any individual ship breaking in two during any one year	1/2 431	1/25 214	1/8 127

* These figures relate to ships of 2 500 tons gross and over.

Table 1.2

Age of Ships that Broke in Two	Tankers	Dry Cargo	Total
Pre-war built	7	–	7
War-built (1940–45)	4	4	8
Post-war built	4	1	5

Of the post-war built ships, one was constructed in 1946, one in 1948, two in 1949 and one in 1952.

It can be seen that the majority (15 ships, or 75% of the total) had been built during the war or earlier, and that even in these early ships the percentage that broke in two was very small.

1.2. OIL DRILLING RIG

The 'Sea Gem' was an off-shore drilling rig for North Sea gas, and consisted of a rectangular pontoon 247 ft long, 90 ft wide and 13 ft deep (75 × 27·5 × 3·95 m) on which were mounted the drilling derrick, operating gear and accommodation. It was provided with 10 steel tubular legs each side. Each of these legs was provided with a pneumatic jacking arrangement whereby the legs could be lowered to the sea bed, and the pontoon could be hoisted clear of the water, so that the rig became a fixed platform for drilling operations. Twelve jacks were disposed around each leg between upper and lower gripper rings, also operated pneumatically. Alternate gripping of these rings, followed by extension or compression of the jacks enabled the barge to be raised or lowered on the legs about 1 foot at each cycle of operation.

At about 1345 hours on Monday, 27th December 1965, during operations preliminary to jacking down the pontoon, after completing drilling operations, the rig collapsed, capsized and sank. There were 32 men on board at the time, 19 of whom lost their lives.

The Tribunal set up by the Ministry of Power to enquire into the causes of the accident found that 'the disaster was initiated by brittle fracture of the tie bars at below yield stress.'[4]

The tie bars referred to formed the suspension links transferring the weight of the barge on to the ten legs via the upper gripper rings of the pneumatic jacking systems. There were four tie bars symmetrically disposed around each leg. Examinations and tests carried out by Lloyd's Register of Shipping showed that each tie bar had been flame-cut from steel plate to the shape shown in Fig. 1.4, with relatively small fillet radii (3/16 in) (4·8 mm) at the upper, or 'spade', end. There was evidence of cracks in attempted weld repairs both at the fillets and at other positions on the shanks. Charpy

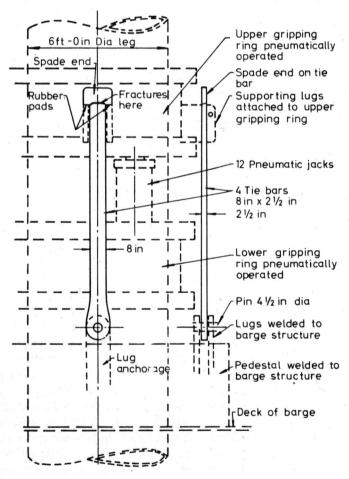

Fig. 1.4. *Sea Gem—Typical tie bar*

V-notch tests on the steel gave low impact values at 0° C i.e., 8–23 ft lb (1·1–3·2 kg m)—associated with high crystallinity. A photoelastic investigation showed a stress concentration factor of 7·0 at the spade end fillet. All these factors were conducive to brittle fracture at the low temperature 37° F (3° C) prevailing on the day of the collapse. The tribunal concluded that after one or more of the tie bars had failed in this way, dynamic forces would have been released, which, once set in motion, would lead rapidly to the collapse of the whole structure.

1.3. LAND STRUCTURES IN GENERAL

Structures on land are too varied for statistical treatment but it may be worthwhile to give some rough idea of the relative extent to which brittle fractures in each type of structure have aroused sufficient interest to be reported in the engineering literature.

A report[5] was compiled by Professor Shank at the Massachusetts Institute of Technology covering the years 1886 to 1951 and including a bibliography listing 138 references to the relevant literature, gathered from many countries. Some of the cited publications discuss questions relating to brittle fracture in general but most of them refer to individual cases, affecting altogether 57 separate structures. Of the failures described and illustrated in the report, 5 took place during the acceptance tests of the structures, 11 during the first year of service, 15 between the second and fifth years inclusive, 5 in still older structures and 26 at unstated ages.

Abridgements of a selected few of the descriptions included in Shank's report are given below together with notes based on other sources cited.

The earliest of the examples mentioned by Shank is a water standpipe 250 ft (76 m) high which collapsed during acceptance tests. A later one is the collapse in Boston, Mass., in 1919 of a tank containing molasses, 50 ft (15·2 m) high and of 90 ft (27·4 m) diameter, three years old, resulting in serious loss of life and damage to property. The suddenness of the failure led expert witnesses for the defence, at the enquiry which followed, to claim that the cause must have been a bomb planted by agitators. After six years of testimony and argument the Auditor presiding over the enquiry decided, however, that the tank had failed by 'overstress'.[5]

1.4. LIQUID STORAGE TANKS

It is interesting to contrast the uncertainties of these early investigations with the more assured approach to an explanation of failure that was possible when a simple land structure of a common type, namely a welded cylindrical oil tank of 140 ft (42·5 m) diameter and 54 ft (16·4 m) high, collapsed at Fawley, Hants, in 1952. Even here—to quote the final paragraph of the lucid and very revealing report[6]—'careful investigation failed to reveal any indications of a shock, blow or impact of any form; consequently the precise cause of the start of the fracture which resulted in the failure of the tank cannot at present be ascertained'. It is notable also that another tank similar to the first failed within a few weeks.

The cylindrical shell of this tank was built of steel plates supplied to B.S.13, butt welded together both horizontally and vertically and arranged in nine circular courses (strakes). The plates in the bottom course were $1\frac{3}{32}$ in (28 mm) thick and those in the remaining eight courses decreased progressively in thickness to $\frac{1}{4}$ in (6·3 mm) in the top course. The strakes were so placed as to have all their surfaces flush on the inside of the tank. During construction a 'weld prober' sample had been cut out of the weld seam between the first and second strakes, and the hole so formed had been made good by welding. During the execution of a 'full head' water test after erection a vertical crack developed at the position where the 'prober' sample had been repaired; the crack extending 15 in (380 mm) upwards into the second strake and 9 in (230 mm) downwards into the bottom strake at a place containing a 28 in (710 mm) manhole. After the water level had been lowered the ends of this crack were drilled and 24 hr later the crack was cut out and re-welded. Twelve days after this the test was recommenced, the ambient temperature being then just above freezing and the seawater used for testing being at 40° F (4·5° C). When the water reached a level of 48 ft (14·6 m) the tank burst, releasing its entire contents through a fracture extending vertically through the full height of the tank shell, the bottom strake being torn away from the base plate along a wavy line, and eventually the shell fell and flattened out on the ground (Fig. 1.5).

Fig. 1.5. *General view of collapsed tank showing waviness of edge of bottom plate*

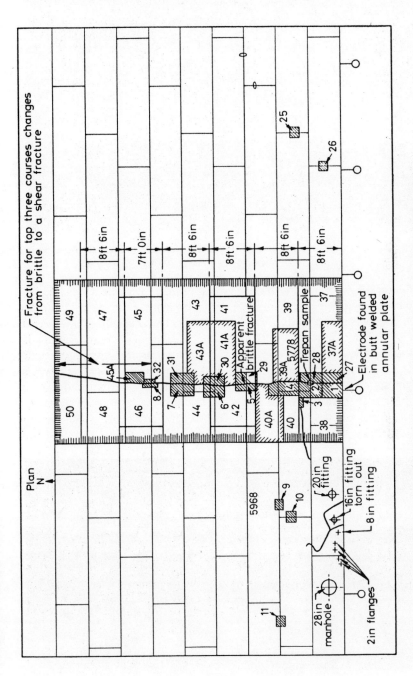

Fig. 1.6. *Diagrammatic view of primary fracture which caused collapse of tank*

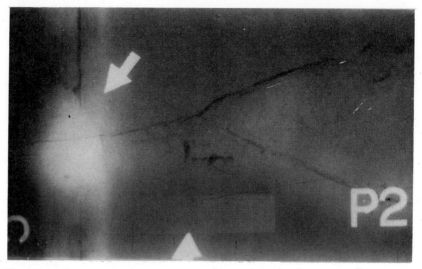

Fig. 1.7. *Radiograph of branching crack in repaired area (By courtesy of National and Vulcan Engineering Insurance Group)*

Subsequent examinations revealed that primary fracture (Fig. 1.6) had started as a branching crack (Fig. 1.7) which originated near the inside surface of the plate where the 'weld prober' sample had been cut out. It then passed through the thickness of the plate to the outside of the tank, gradually becoming oblique on either side of the starting point before progressing through the centre of the plate in each direction and then becoming a typical brittle fracture with chevrons (see page 33) pointing towards the origin. In the uppermost three courses of plates the fracture changed to the shear type (Fig. 1.8). It is noteworthy that after traversing the short weld used for repairing the weld prober hole the fracture did not follow the weld, but

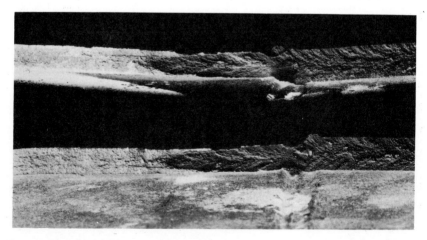

Fig. 1.8. *Photograph of shear-type fracture (By courtesy of National and Vulcan Engineering Insurance Group)*

passed entirely through the unwelded parent plate material to the top and bottom of the tank (Fig. 1.6).

An investigation[7] of the numbers, size distribution and failures of oil tanks in the United States up to 1952 revealed that the total number of tanks with capacities of not less than 55 000 barrels (310 000 ft^3 (8 750 m^3)), which can be visualised as a tank of about 100 ft (30·5 m) diameter 40 ft (12·2 m) high) then existing was approximately 6 000. There had been 32 failures of such tanks, of which brief particulars are given,[7] 19 being partial and 12 complete. In an accompanying discussion[8] of the actuarial and economic aspects it is shown that, assuming the number of tanks in service each year was proportional to the refining capacity of the industry in that year, there had been one brittle failure per 3 400 tank-years in service. Statistical prediction based on the Poisson distribution pointed to a close correlation between the numbers of failures predictable on this basis and the actual numbers, which suggests that there is a strong element of chance in this matter, although in about one half of the failures some readily evident defect of design or workmanship could be shown to have been related to the initiation of a crack. There have been many fewer failures in tanks built since 1925 than in earlier ones. In approximately two-thirds of the failed tanks the lowest course was of $\frac{5}{8}$ in (16 mm) plate and in the remainder it was thicker.

More tanks failed in crude oil service than in any other, and with one unrelated exception all the failures occurred between November and March. There are two good reasons for this (also stated by Shank[5]): namely that the lower the ambient temperature the greater is the likelihood that thermal stresses will be built up so as to start a crack and the more likely the steel is to fail in a brittle manner if a crack does start. In such a tank, the temperature at the bottom, which rests on the ground or on a sand pad, is fairly constant. The contents of the tank are at best poor conductors of heat and their increased viscosity as they cool makes them even better insulators. In crude oils, particularly, the heavy fractions tend to separate close to the tank wall, thus insulating the shell and subjecting it to a thermal stress occasioned by changes in atmospheric temperatures.

In one of the American failures[5] which took place in 1943, a riveted oil tank had been leaking and in order to admit a wheelbarrow when repairing it, a large triangular hole had been flame cut in the bottom course of plates. The hole was afterwards closed by electrically welding into place the piece of steel that had been cut out. Parts of the weld were afterwards found to be of poor quality. Moreover, the welding of a patch into a solid plate is known to cause a high degree of constraint, with high residual stress. Later, when the tank was nearly full of oil, the resulting notch effect combined with a low ambient temperature had been sufficient to initiate a brittle fracture in the weld, which then propagated up and down through the solid metal of the patch and original plate.

Another example of failure, fortunately not catastrophic, occurred in an oil tank in Europe.[5] In the course of erection the contractor had chipped flush the weld overlay at the seams inside the tank, besides which it was evident that an excessive amount of hammering had been done to correct distortion of the plates. Several weeks after completion, while the tank was still empty, the ambient temperature fell to $-4°$ C and a large number of cracks developed. These had originated at the chipped or hammered surfaces of the welds and extended transversely across them into the plates, which decreased in thickness upwards from $\frac{5}{8}$ in to $\frac{1}{4}$ in (16 to 6·3 mm), for a distance of about 3 in (76 mm). Except in one instance, the cracks occurred in plates more than $\frac{1}{2}$ in (12·8 mm) thick. Failure was attributed to a combination of:

1. tranverse surface fissures caused by the chipping tool,
2. tensile residual welding stresses acting normally to the fissures along the line of the weld, and
3. the increased notch sensitivity of the steel due to the fall in temperature and to the work hardening of the weld surface layers by excessive chipping and hammering.

(Note: Work hardening is further discussed in Chapter 3.)

1.5. GAS PRESSURE VESSELS

A container filled with a gas under pressure has considerably more potential energy available to propagate a crack than has a similar container filled with a relatively incompressible liquid. This has been shown clearly by tests made at UKAEA.[9]

Around 1944 several brittle failures occurred where this circumstance applied both in spherical and in cylindrical vessels. One serious instance[10] which occurred at Schenectady, New York, was a spherical tank of 38 ft 6 in (11·7 m) diameter, designed to hold hydrogen at a pressure of 50 lb/in² (3 450 N/m²) built of semi-killed steel plates 0·66 in (16·7 mm) thick welded together. The manhole had been made up of two sub-assemblies, one being the bolt flange of the neck and the other being the collar and sphere plate. The latter, of $\frac{3}{4}$ in sheared cold rolled plate, was welded in place on the site. Acceptance tests had shown no leaks. After three months service, the sphere burst catastrophically into twenty fragments, following a temperature rise of 27° F (15° C) in seven hours up to 10° F ($-12°$ C) at the time of failure, when the internal pressure was about 50 lb/in² (3 450 N/m²). The total length of brittle fracture was 650 ft (198 m) and the chevron markings (see page 33) all pointed back to the manhole which was the origin of the fracture and where the intensity of the stress had been greatest. (Fig. 1.9.) Only a few feet of the fracture followed along welded seams, but at the manhole neck, where several old radial cracks were found, the shrinkage of the heavy weld had left residual stresses approaching the yield point of the semi-killed steel, which behaved in a brittle manner at the existing temperature.

In Cleveland, Ohio, an even more disastrous failure occurred at about the same time, causing 128 deaths and $6 800 000 worth of damage. Three double-shelled spherical tanks had been built to hold liquified natural gas

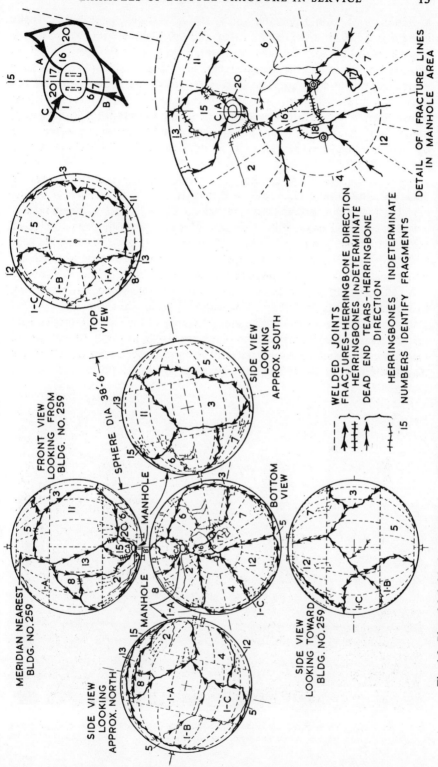

Fig. 1.9. Plot of failed hydrogen sphere at Schenectady, N.Y. showing path of brittle tears determined from the herringbone markings (Welding Journal 24, 3 Mar. 1945)

at 5 lb/in^2 (345 N/m^2) pressure and $-260°$ F ($-162°$ C) their outer shells being of welded open-hearth mild steel and lined with a 3 ft (910 mm) layer of granulated cork in a vapour-tight space, having inside this a 57 ft (17·3 m) diameter storage sphere of welded nickel alloy steel. Each sphere was supported on twelve columns. The fractures were of the brittle type and the evidence indicated that they had a great many origins.[5] Analysis of the steel showed that it conformed to specifications, but one group of investigators pointed out that for such very low temperature applications it would have been more usual, even at that time, to prefer austenitic stainless steel or a non-ferrous alloy.

There have been other examples of brittle fracture in pressure vessels made of alloy steels. One case, reported in 1962,[11] occurred during the construction of the nuclear power station at Chinon in France, where serious cracking occurred in the 4 in thick wall of a large pressure vessel made of 1·26% Mn, 0·60% Mo steel. It had originated in the transformed zone near a circumferential weld and had propagated through parent plate of which the notch ductility had been impaired by prolonged stress relief heat treatment.

A failure occurred in a large boiler at the Sizewell power station, during hydrostatic testing, in 1963.[12] The causes of this were not obvious but abundant evidence associated the great majority of the fracture origins with the presence of the thermal sleeves which are visible in Fig. 1.10; yet careful searches carried out by several different methods revealed no defects at the places where these sleeves had been welded to the boiler plates.

Fig. 1.10. *Failure of boiler No. 2A under hydrostatic test (By courtesy of West of Scotland Iron and Steel Institute)*

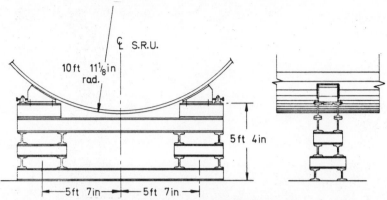

Fig. 1.11. *General arrangement of support pier*

The boiler, which with its water content weighed approximately 1 200 tons (1 220 000 kg), had a cylindrical shell 62 ft (18·8 m) long and of 22 ft 6 in (6·8 m) internal diameter, fabricated by welding from Mn–Cr–Mo–V steel plates $2\frac{1}{4}$ in (57 mm) thick. At the time of the test it rested on chocks (Fig. 1.11) and it was found that the failure had been initiated by these shifting so as to cause a redistribution of the hydrostatically imposed stresses, thus precipitating the fracture of the shell along the line of the existing stress concentrations.

Fig. 1.12. *Failure by brittle fracture of thick-walled cylindrical pressure vessel during hydraulic test (By courtesy of John Thompson Ltd., Wolverhampton)*

Fig. 1.13. *A two-ton segment of the vessel in Fig. 1.12 which was thrown 152 ft (By courtesy of John Thompson, Ltd., Wolverhampton)*

In December, 1965 a large thick-walled cylindrical pressure vessel intended to be used in an ammonia plant at Immingham failed by brittle fracture during hydraulic test at the manufacturer's works in Wolverhampton. Fig. 1.12 is a photograph of the failure as a whole and Fig. 1.13 shows a two-ton segment which was thrown 152 ft (46 m).

The vessel had a plain shell of 5 ft 7 in (1·7 m) inside diameter and 52 ft 8½ in (16 m) overall length, made up of ten cylindrical strakes fabricated in plates of Mn–Cr–Mo–V steel 5⅞ in (149 mm) thick with forged end closures of similar material, each of the three sections being furnace stress relieved and the joining welds locally stress relieved. It weighed 164 ton (167 000 kg) and the flange ring 14 ton (14 300 kg). The design pressure was 5 100 lb/in^2 (35·2 N/mm^2) at 120° C and a hydrostatic test pressure of 7 240 lb/in^2 (50 N/mm^2) was specified. The ambient temperature at the time of failure was +7° C. One end forging and three strakes of body plates were extensively fractured.

A report[13] since published gives full details of the extensive investigation carried out following the failure, from which it was concluded that brittle fracture had been initiated at two of three very small pre-existing cracks discovered on the forging side of the weld in the heat-effected zone of the submerged arc weld which connected the large forging at one end to the adjacent strake. It was also concluded that the correct stress relief treatment had not been applied and that this contributed to very poor fracture resistance in the weld metal.

Further examples of failures in pressure vessels which have been fully investigated may be found in Pellini and Puzak's report.[14]

1.6. PENSTOCKS AND PIPELINES

These two kinds of structure resemble one another in being closed channels through which fluids move under pressure and in that their transverse dimensions are small compared with their length.

In a penstock or water pipeline the fluid is a liquid sufficiently dense and incompressible to transmit severe transient shock waves with high velocity. In a gas pipeline, on the other hand, pressure waves travel in the gas more slowly than a crack can extend in the steel. In either case, therefore, a sufficient supply of energy may be available from the fluid contained within the penstock or pipeline to maintain the propagation of a crack for great distances.

This action was exemplified in a penstock, built in 1950, serving the Anderson Ranch Dam in Idaho, which consisted essentially of a 15 ft (4·57 m) diameter pipe built of 'firebox quality' steel sections fabricated in the field and erected by welding inside a concrete lined tunnel of 20 ft (6·1 m) diameter.[5] The penstock was designed for a static water head of 326 ft (99·5 m) plus a waterhammer head of 94 ft (28·7 m), amounting to a total head of 420 ft (128 m) or 183 lb/in^2 (1·26 N/m^2). Hydrostatic pressure tests were to be performed at 225 lb/in^2 (1·55 N/m^2). On the third portion tested, when a pressure of 220 lb/in^2 (1·52 N/m^2) was reached, a crack appeared which ran across three pipe sections, having plate thicknesses of $1\frac{5}{16}$ in (33·4 mm) and $1\frac{9}{16}$ in (39·8 mm). This crack was 50 ft (15·2 m) long, running through the plate parallel but not closer than 5 in (127 mm) to a longitudinal weld. There were lateral branching fractures which passed through two stiffener ring supports, one at each end of the crack. The resistance offered by these rings to the propagation of the crack had the effect of changing its course.

All specifications had been met and investigations showed no defects in the plates. Apparently the fracture had been started by the notch effect from very irregular bands of a repair weld in a welded girth joint. Another small crack radiated from the same point and the chevron markings all pointed to this source.[5]

Details of other fractures in early penstocks, and the history of the development of penstock design from 1937 to 1967 have been given by Muller[15] and Felix.[16]

1.7. BRIDGES

During the years immediately before the second World War about fifty bridges of the Vierendeel type were built across the Albert Canal in Belgium. Such a bridge is a truss in which the upper and lower chords are interconnected not by diagonal members but by vertical posts rigidly joined to them and subject, like the chords, to bending moments. The steel used was of the Belgian St.42 (Bessemer) type and all the connections were made by welding. The manner of welding, and the sequences adopted later attracted some criticism. For instance, in the bridge at Kaulille, constructed with its chords composed not of plates, but of rolled 'I' beams as shown in Fig. 1.14, one end had lifted 3 cm as a result of weld contractions while still supported on falsework. The welders had corrected the alignment as they worked.

Serious cracks occurred in several of these bridges during cold weather.

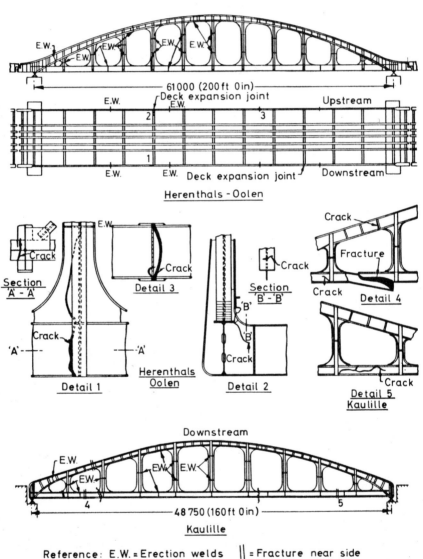

Reference: E.W. = Erection welds || = Fracture near side
⸘ = Fracture far side

Fig. 1.14. *Details of failures in two welded Vierendeel truss bridges (Railway Gazette 72, 10 Mar, 8, 1940)*

In the Herenthals–Oolen bridge (also included in Fig. 1.14) the cracking was accompanied by three loud reports in succession. One of the cracks was 7 ft (2·1 m) long and opened to 1 in (25 mm), but the bridge did not collapse and five hours later a locomotive passed over it without incident.

A more serious and spectacular failure was that of the Hasselt bridge of 244 ft (74·5 m) span. After fourteen months service the bridge collapsed under the load of a tramcar and some pedestrians, about six minutes elapsing between the loud report of the first crack and the falling of the bridge. According to witnesses one of the cross girders first began to fall off and a big crack then opened in the lower chord of the bridge, thus transmitting all the load to the upper chord which acted as an arch throwing a horizontal thrust onto the abutments, as was revealed by big masses of masonry shearing off. Cracks then appeared in the upper chord and the whole bridge collapsed into three portions. The outer portions fell on both sides of the Canal, which may have been the cause of a number of secondary fractures both in the chords and in the verticals. The weather at the time was cold, the temperature being −20° C (−4° F).

Probably because of the war, no complete report was published by the Commission set up to enquire into these failures, but various studies of it have been published in several countries[17, 18, 19] and others to which references may be found in the bibliography appended to the survey by Shank.[5]

The Duplessis bridge at Three Rivers in Quebec, completed in 1947, was of continuous welded plate girder deck construction, comprising six spans of 180 ft (55 m) and two of 150 ft (45·8 m). After twenty-seven months service a crack was discovered in one of the girders near the east end of the bridge, and while this was being repaired a similar crack was found in an identical part near the west end. Both cracks were brittle. They originated in top flange plates close to butt welded joints and travelled towards the centre of the girder web. The eastern break buckled the web and lower flange. The western break stopped because of the tensile action of the slab reinforcement. Nearly a year later, and two weeks after everything had been reported satisfactory following a continuous ten-day inspection, one of the 150-ft (45·8 m) girders at the west end fractured in a brittle manner and collapsed into the river when the temperature was −30° F (−35° C). The investigation which followed revealed that the broken flange plates were of poor quality rimming steel, unsuitable for welding and contained high local concentrations of carbon and sulphur, besides many slag inclusions.[20]

The failure of four girders in the Kings bridge at Melbourne, Australia, is of special interest for several reasons, not least the thoroughness and cogency of the report[21] produced by the Royal Commission which investigated the incident. The bridge had been designed to carry two parallel but independent roadways on a curved alignment and at varying levels over a river, a railway, six other roads and the intervening ground. The structure comprised four lines of plate-web main girders, mostly of about 100 ft (30·5 m) span and 5 ft (1·52 m) deep, supporting a reinforced concrete deck over their top flanges. In most of the spans the ends of the longitudinal girders were suspended between the ends of steel cantilevers projecting on each side of the intervening piers.

In July 1962, fifteen months after the bridge had been opened to traffic, a loaded vehicle of about 45 tons (45 800 kg) weight crossing one of the spans caused it to collapse suddenly and to sag approximately 1 ft (300 mm), further subsidence being prevented by the concrete deck. Subsequent examination showed that all four of the suspended girders at this point had typical brittle fractures (Fig. 1.15) approximately 16 ft (4·9 m) from one end, and that three of the girders had similar fractures at corresponding positions 16 ft (4·9 m) from the other end. The fractures had started from cracks in the parent metal of the flange plates at the tees of fillet welds connecting the ends of the flange cover plates to the main flange (Fig. 1.16). It was established beyond doubt that the ultimate dramatic collapse represented merely the last stage in a 'cascade' pattern of fractures which had taken many months to reach the point where final collapse ensued. Each crack had started in the heat affected zone of the second weld bead and continued into the parent metal of the lower flanges; running transversely to the length of the flange at a position of stress concentration associated with the sudden change of thickness.

The Royal Commission found that a variety of circumstances had contributed to the accident, some being technical and—what is equally instructive— some deriving from faulty organisation of the work and deficiencies of communication between the many parties concerned, namely the public authority which had prepared the outline scheme for the bridge, the group of four consulting engineers who had sub-contracted to complete the design, the

Fig. 1.15. *Fracture of girder W.14–4, showing cover plate end (By courtesy of Agent-General for Victoria, Australia)*

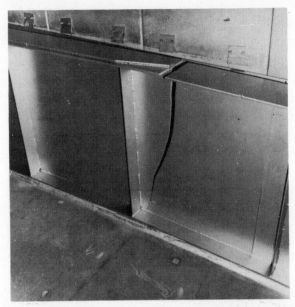

Fig. 1.16. *Fracture in girder W.14–1 (By courtesy of Agent-General for Victoria, Australia)*

main contractor, the firm sub-contracting to fabricate and erect the steel-work, and the steelmakers.

In order to allow higher design stresses so as to lighten the bridge and realise a net saving in cost, a high tensile steel in accordance with the old BS.968:1941 was specified. That specification had been issued as a War Emergency Standard and did not call for impact testing or other control over notch ductility. Appreciating this, the public authority concerned had demanded impact tests as an additional requirement, but in the actual construction these tests were not adequately performed. (It should be noted here that the old British Standard Specification has since been superseded by BS.968:1962, and later by BS.4360:1968, which provides for improved weld-ability and for impact testing at user's option.)

1.8. MISCELLANEOUS CASES OF BRITTLE FRACTURE

Among the other structures and machines described by Shank[5] as having failed by brittle fracture are a methane column 43 ft (13·1 m) high in which the carbon steel plate, of 'firebox quality', was very notch-brittle and the side connections had acted as stress raisers; also a welded steel stack nearly 178 ft (54·2 m) high in which the hoop stress has been augmented in cold weather by expansion of the brick lining and the effect aggravated by wind oscillations. Yet another was in the boom of a power shovel.

Boyd[22] has given brief details regarding thirteen cases of brittle failure in turbo-generator sets that occurred (two of them in England) during the years 1948–58. In such a machine both the turbine and the generator are sub-

Fig. 1.17. *General view of the H.P. end of the turbo-generator with other debris after the breakdown*

stantial and complicated assemblies of castings and forgings, and as the electrical load of a modern alternator may exceed 500 000 hp (370 000 kW) the failure of a component can have devastating results. In five of the thirteen cases the failures were attributed to overspeeding, either deliberate in overspeed trip testing, or accidental due to governor failure. In five cases

Fig. 1.18. *Alternator forging pieced together*

(a) (b)

Fig. 1.19. *(a) Low-pressure turbine wheel adjacent to that in (b). (b) One low-pressure turbine wheel, bent but unbroken*

the prime failure was brittle fracture in the 'end bell', which was of austenitic (non-magnetic) steel, and the fractures, which were intergranular in character, has originated at ventilation holes drilled in the bells. Fig. 1.17, taken from an article by Rotherham,[23] shows the debris after such a failure caused by a governor fault which allowed the normal service speed of 3 000 rev/min to rise to about 5 000 rev/min. Fig. 1.18 shows the alternator forging pieced together and Fig. 1.19 shows two adjacent low pressure turbine wheels.

Further brittle failures were described and discussed at a conference in Glasgow.[24]

1.9. SUMMARY

Table 1.3 below is a list in a date order of the cases mentioned in this Chapter. This is, of course, far from being a complete list of the brittle fractures on record.

Table 1.3

Date of failure	Type and location of structure	Riveted or welded	Main cause of failure of chief point of interest
1866	Water standpipe, New York	R	Earliest case found in the literature, ascribed to use of steel plates at a time when wrought iron was more useful
1889	Sealing tank of gasholder, New York	R	Fracture through body of plates, not along rivet lines
1919	Molasses tank, Boston, Mass.	R	Overstressing with catastrophic consequences
1934	Oil tank, U.S.A.	W	Temperature difference between bottom and sides in sudden cold weather
1938–50	Vierendeel truss bridges, Belgium	W	Various and disputed causes including faulty welding, residual stresses, notch-brittle steel

Table 1.3—continued

Date of failure	Type and location of structure	Riveted or welded	Main cause of failure or chief point of interest
1942	Oil tank, Fawley, Hants.	W	Failure initiated from a repair weld
1942–46	Merchant ships built in U.S.A.	W	Notch sensitivity of steel
1943	Oil tank, U.S.A.	R	Notch effect in welded patch
1943	Spherical pressure vessel, Schenectady	W	Stress concentrations and residual stresses near yield point of brittle semi-killed steel
1944	Pressure vessel, Cleveland, Ohio	W	Multiple origins. Very low temperature. ($-162°$ C) steel probably unsuitable
1945	Methane column operating at $-110°$ C, U.S.A.	W	Notches in defective welds and in carbon steel plate, stress concentrations at side openings
	High pressure gas pipelines, U.S.A.		Very long cracks follow a sinusoidal pattern
1949–63	Merchant ships built elsewhere than in U.S.A.	R and W	Notch sensitivity of steel
1948–58	Turbo-generators	W	Various causes including crack initiation at drilled holes
1949	Plate girders of Duplessis Bridge, Quebec	W	Poor quality rimming steel unsuitable for welding
1949	Power shovel boom, U.S.A.	W	Crack along transverse butt weld initiated by proximity of a diaphragm inside the boom
1949	Power shovel dipper, U.S.A.	W	
1950	Penstock, Idaho	W	Notch effect of irregular beads in repair weld
1951	Stack, Chicago	W	Brittle behaviour at low temperature. Expansion of hot lining increased the hoop stress
1952	Oil tank, Europe	W	Cracks initiated at fissures left from hammering and chipping, propagation aided by work hardening effect and residual stress
1954	Tanker 'World Concord'		Separate consecutive fractures in notch-brittle plates joined together in same transverse plane of ship
1962	Plate-web girders of Kings Bridge, Melbourne	W	Welding of BS.968 (1941) steel not locally understood and tests not properly performed
1962	Pressure vessel, Chinon, France	W	Notch ductility of alloy steel impaired by prolonged stress-relief heat treatment
1963	Large boiler, Sizewell nuclear reactor	W	Failure initiated by redistribution of stresses imposed by hydrostatic test, due to movement of supporting chocks
1965	Thick-walled cylindrical pressure vessel	W	Fracture initiated during hydraulic test in pre-existing cracks in HAZ of submerged arc weld connecting strake to end forging
1965	Drilling rig 'Sea Gem', North Sea	W	Fracture initiated in tie-bars flame cut from steel plate

1.10. REVIEW OF LESSONS LEARNED FROM SERVICE EXPERIENCE

The cases of brittle fracture in service mentioned in Sections 1.1–1.9, as well as many others, have been very thoroughly studied and the following observations emerge.

Brittle fracture has affected steel structures in practically all branches of engineering. Although its incidence has been fairly low, the risk is clearly too great to be ignored in all but trivial types of structures, and precautions are imperative in any structure the failure of which would involve serious consequences. Observations of the behaviour of structures in service, and laboratory studies of the phenomenon, have shown that the occurrence of brittle fracture is a matter of probability rather than of predictable cause and effect. The risk increases with a number of conducive factors, some of which are discussed below. Many structures known to be operating under conditions that conduce to brittle fracture have survived, while others in which the conditions appeared to be satisfactory have failed.

Stress. Most of the service fractures have occurred at moderate or low nominal stresses, within the ranges usually considered safe for the structures affected.

Temperature. A strong correlation has been observed, showing that the fractures became more brittle, more frequent and more extensive towards the lower end of the range of service temperatures.

Notches. The initiation of the majority of the brittle fractures that have occurred in service, has been associated with notch effects due to discontinuities inherent in the design, to faults in welds, or to accidental damage.

Thickness. The studies of service fractures suggest that the thicker plates and sections are more liable to brittle fracture than the thinner. The matter is further discussed in Section 3.1.4.

Welding. Although most of the brittle fractures in welded structures have originated at or near welds, they have not in general been due to simple failure of the welds themselves. Few of the reports collected gave details of the characteristics of the weld metal, but it emerged that faulty welding had caused the initiation of some of the fractures. None of the primary fractures followed a weld, either in the weld metal or in the heat affected zone. In four cases it was noted that the qualities of the weld had helped to arrest the fractures.

Impact. Although many service brittle fractures have occurred under essentially static loading, some have been associated with shock or impact loading.

Fatigue. Only a small proportion of service brittle fractures are definitely known to have originated at fatigue cracks. Others may have done so without the fact having been established by the investigations. Many fractures have occurred under conditions that preclude fatigue as a factor.

Materials properties. The examination and testing of materials involved in service fractures, and also of samples taken from unfractured structures, have clearly shown that the response of different steels to the factors enumerated above varies considerably, so that the liability to brittle fracture under given conditions is much higher in some steels than in others. This liability is known to be a function of temperature, so that a given sample of steel behaves in a brittle manner at some temperatures and in a ductile manner at higher temperatures. The range within which the behaviour changes from ductile to brittle may be well within the normal range of ambient temperatures. This leads to the conclusion that selection of materials is a potent factor in controlling the risk, and this point is fully developed in other parts of this book.

References

1. *The design and methods of construction of welded steel merchant vessels: Final report of a Board of Investigation convened by order of the Secretary of the Navy* US Government Printing Office, Washington (1947)
2. HODGSON, J. and BOYD, G. M., 'Brittle fracture in welded ships', *Trans. Royal Institution of Naval Architects*, **100**, 141–180 (1958)
3. BOYD, G. M. and BUSHELL, T. W., 'Hull structural steel; the unification of the requirements of seven classifications societies', *Trans. Royal Institution of Naval Architects*, **103** (1961)
4. 'Report of the Inquiry into the Causes of the Accident to the Drilling Rig *Sea Gem*,' *HMSO Cmnd* 3409 (1967)
5. SHANK, M. E., 'A critical survey of brittle failure in carbon plate steel structures other than ships', *National Academy of Sciences/National Research Council, Washington* (1953) also *Welding Research Council (USA) Bulletin Series* No 17
6. 'Failure of large welded oil storage tank', *National Boiler and General Insurance Co. Ltd., Manchester* (1954)
7. SAMANS, C. H., 'Results of the survey of the study group on oil storage tank failures', *American Petroleum Institute meeting at Houston, Texas* (May, 1954)
8. GITZENDANNER, F. A., 'Some economic aspects of the oil storage tank failure problem', *American Petroleum Institute meeting at Houston, Texas* (May, 1954)
9. BEVITT, E., COWAN, A. and STOTT, A. L., *Journal British Nuclear Energy Society*, **3**, 16 (1964)
10. BROWN, A. L. and SMITH, J. B., 'Failure of a Spherical Hydrogen Storage Tank', *The Welding Journal*, **24**, No 3, 235 (March, 1945)
11. LAMIRAL, G. and LECLER, R., 'La réalisation à Chinon des caissons de Réacteurs EDF1 et EDF2', *Soudage et Techniques Connexes*, **16**, No 11/12 (November/December, 1962)
12. 'Special report on failure of a boiler during hydrostatic test at Sizewell Nuclear Power Station' (containing metallurgical investigation by HARRIS, H., engineering investigation by HAFTKE, J. J., and tests on Mn–Cr–Mo–V steels by other investigators). *West of Scotland Iron and Steel Institute* (1964)
13. *BWRA Bulletin*, **7**, No 6 (June, 1966)
14. PELLINI, W. S. and PUZAK, P. P., 'Fracture Analysis Diagram Procedures for the Fracture-Safe Engineering Design of Steel Structures', *NRL Report* 5920 (March, 1963)

15. MULLER, W., 'Materials and Welding in old Hydro Station Penstocks', *Sulzer Technical Review*, **3**, 131 (1967)
16. FELIX, W., 'Fracture Behaviour of High Strength Weldable Steels for Penstock Fabrication', *Sulzer Technical Review*, **3**, 187 (1967)
17. BONDY, O., 'The collapse of an all-welded bridge at Hasselt, Belgium', *Engineering*, 669–671 (17th June, 1938)
18. REEVE, L., 'Examination of welded steel specimens from the Hasselt bridge', *Quarterly Trans. Institute of Welding*, **3**, 3–13 (1940)
19. BUSH, H. and REULECKE, W., 'Investigation of failure in a welded bridge', *Welding Journal*, 25(8) *Research Supplement*, 463s–465s, translated from *Stahl und Eisen*, 62 (1942)
20. MERRITT, F. S., 'Engineering News Record' (Canada) Vol **146**(6), 23–24 (8th February, 1951)
21. 'Report of Royal Commission into the Failure of Kings Bridge'. *Presented to Parliament (of) Victoria (Australia)*, *Melbourne, 1963*. A. C. Brooks, Government Printers, Melbourne (1963)
22. BOYD, G. M., 'Brittle Fracture in Steel', *Admiralty Advisory Committee on Structural Steel, Report* **No 3**, HMSO (1962)
23. ROTHERHAM, L., 'The brittle fracture of steel', *Endeavour*, **24**, 91 (January, 1965)
24. 'Conference on Failures in Large Steel Structures', *West of Scotland Iron & Steel Inst.* (May 1968)

CHAPTER 2

CHARACTERISTICS AND MODES OF FRACTURE

There are many different mechanisms by which a metal may break or fracture, that is, to separate into two or more distinct parts. Brittle or low stress fracture, with which this book is mainly concerned, is only one of these mechanisms. In order to describe it clearly however it is necessary to consider briefly some of the other mechanisms of fracture.

All metals, whether pure or in the form of alloys, i.e. composed of several metallic and/or non metallic elements, normally have a poly-crystalline structure.

In each crystal (or grain), the atoms are arranged in a regular 3-dimensional array, which in iron and steel is of a cubical form. The orientations of these arrays, although uniform in an individual crystal, vary from crystal to crystal in a random manner.

When a metal consisting of an aggregate of crystals is subjected to load at ambient temperatures, the crystals first deform in an elastic manner, that is, they are able to regain their original form once the load is removed. If the load is increased beyond a certain level, yielding occurs, that is the crystals deform in a permanent, non-elastic or plastic manner by slip, namely the movement of atomic planes relative to each other. As this process continues, the force required to cause further slip increases. This process is known as 'work hardening' (see p. 40). As the load is increased, further deformation occurs and eventually some crystals break, which ultimately leads to complete fracture of the metal.

2.1. FRACTURE MECHANISMS

The fracture mechanism of polycrystalline materials under applied stress may take one of several distinct forms namely:

1. *Shear* is the process in which planes of atoms slide over one another, so that the crystals deform and elongate, thereby reducing their cross-sections so that the resulting fracture is similar to that observed in the cup-and-cone tensile fracture of mild steel. This is illustrated in Fig. 2.1,[1] in which it can be seen that the crystals (standing vertically in the illustration) have elongated and broken. The resulting fracture surface has a silky or dull fibrous appearance.

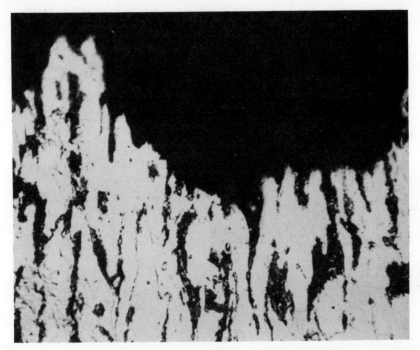

Fig. 2.1. *Fibrous (shear) mode of fracture (× 500) (From some Observations on the Brittle Fracture Problem. Welding Research Council (USA) Bulletin, 57, 1960)*

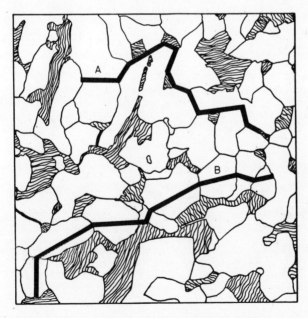

Fig. 2.2. *Diagrammatic representation of (a) intercrystalline and (b) transcrystalline cracks*

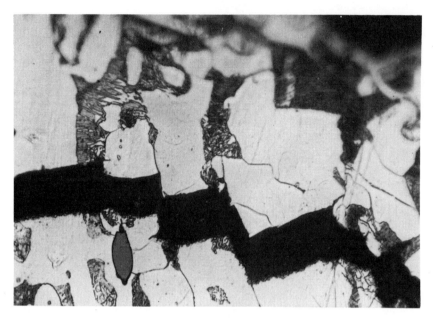

Fig. 2.3. *Cleavage mode of fracture (From West of Scotland Iron and Steel Institute, Conference on Brittle Fracture, 1952)*

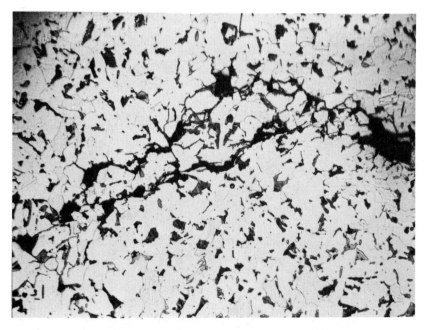

Fig. 2.4. *Showing the normalised low carbon ferrite/pearlite general structure and the intercrystalline complex which constitutes the cracking (By courtesy of the Admiralty Materials Laboratory)*

2. *Cleavage* is the process in which cracking occurs on certain well defined atomic planes with little or no prior plastic deformation. The propagation of cleavage cracks results in a transcrystalline type of failure in the manner shown schematically in Fig. 2.2(b). The appearance of a cleavage crack under the microscope is shown in Fig. 2.3[2] and has a shiny sparkling appearance.

3. *Intercrystalline* fracture occurs by separation along grain (or crystal) boundaries, as also shown schematically in Fig. 2.2(a). The appearance of the fracture surface is somewhat similar to that of cleavage fracture. This fracture mechanism is rare in ordinary structural steels, and only occurs in the presence of certain corrosive environments. It does, however, sometimes occur in weld metal or in the heat affected zone of parent plate, arising from 'hot tearing' which can occur under certain circumstances during cooling after welding. Fig. 2.4 shows a typical example of an intercrystalline fracture.

4. *Fatigue* cracks are caused by the action of cyclic or intermittent loadings. A crack generally forms at a free surface, as a consequence of localised cyclic plastic deformation in some surface grains. See Fig. 2.5(a). It progresses into the body of the material until it is able to grow, normal to the maximum cyclic tensile stress in the loading cycle, by the repeated opening and closing of the crack tip. Fatigue cracks may also be initiated at surface or subsurface inclusions or defects, in which case the fatigue strength depends on the size, shape and dispersion of these flaws rather than on the stress to cause surface slip. Fatigue fracture surfaces have a

Fig. 2.5. *(a) Fatigue fracture of a stud (By courtesy of National Engineering Laboratory, Ministry of Technology)*

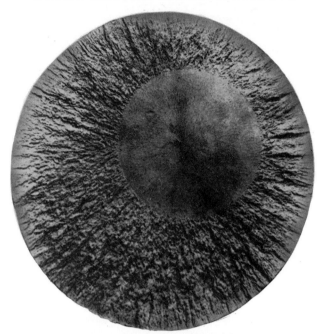

Fig. 2.5. *(b) Steam-hammer piston rod fatigue fracture (Reprinted with permission from Lessells, Strength and Resistance of Metals, 1954, John Wiley and Sons, Inc)*

smooth appearance and markings may be observed which indicate the progressive nature of the process at each stress cycle, or group of cycles. Fatigue cracks usually propagate slowly, compared with brittle cracks, but unless they are detected they may grow to such an extent that they become unstable, and then propagate by fast fracture mechanism. Fig. 2.5(b)[3] shows the fracture of a steam-hammer piston rod. It can be seen that the fracture began as a fatigue crack, and appears as a smooth circular region in the centre of the rod, which at a later stage became a brittle fracture.

2.2. FRACTURE MODE

A more precise description of the geometry of fracture can be made by reference to the three possible components of crack surface displacements. The mode of fracture refers to the direction of the relative motion between the two corresponding crack surfaces during the fracture process. The three possible basic modes of crack surface displacement are shown in Fig. 2.6. In Mode I, often referred to as the opening mode, the crack surfaces move apart perpendicular to each other as shown in Fig. 2.6(a). In Mode II, the forward sliding mode, as shown in Fig. 2.6(b), the two crack surfaces move apart in approximately the same plane in a direction perpendicular to the line of the crack tip. Mode III, the tearing mode, as shown in Fig. 2.6(c), is the mode in which the two corresponding crack surfaces extend in approxi-

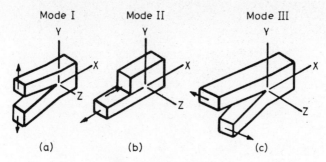

Fig. 2.6. *Modes of fracture*

mately the same plane and in a direction which is parallel to the line of the crack front. These three modes are sufficient to describe all forms of crack surface displacements. Mode I displacements result in a flat type of fracture surface perpendicular to the applied stress axis. Most fatigue and brittle fractures are of this type. Shear or slant fractures are combinations of Modes I and III.

2.2.1. Brittle Fracture

Brittle fracture comprises at least two stages, namely that of crack initiation and that of crack propagation. Brittle fracture is fracture that occurs suddenly with little or no prior deformation, often at nominal computed stresses below the macroscopic yield point or yield strength of the material. Brittle fractures propagate at high speed and in structural steels this is of the order of several thousand feet per second.

The main characteristics of a typical brittle fracture of a mild steel plate are illustrated in Fig. 2.7, which shows two aspects of the same fracture in a steel plate tested under laboratory conditions.[4] Fig. 2.8 is a diagrammatic sketch showing the above characteristics. The process of formation of such fractures is fully described by Boyd.[5] An important characteristic feature of the fracture surface is the 'chevron' pattern, which consists of a system of ridges curving outwards from the centre line of the plate. These ridges, or chevrons, may be regarded as arrowheads with their points on the centre line and invariably pointing towards the origin of the fracture, so providing a reliable indication of its propagation pattern. This can be of great importance in analysis of service failures. While the chevrons are normally symmetrical in plate fractures, they tend to be asymmetrical when fracture has occurred under combined tensile and bending stresses. The surface ridges do not always form chevrons, but they do always lie parallel to the direction in which the fracture front has moved. An example can be seen in Fig. 2.5(b) where the ridges are radial, indicating that the fracture front (outside the fatigue zone) expanded concentrically. In general the more brittle the fracture the less pronounced are the ridges. The surface appearance of a brittle fracture in mild steel is 'crystalline', indicating that the majority of the crystals have separated by a cleavage mechanism, but closer examination indicates that

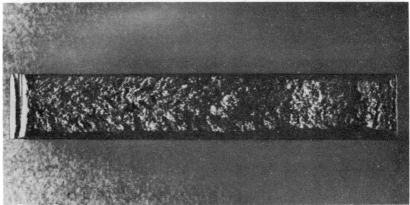

Fig. 2.7. *The main characteristics of a typical brittle fracture of a mild steel plate. (a) perspective view, (b) full-faced view (By courtesy of the Institution of Metallurgists)*

some crystals also separate by shear. In general, the more brittle the fracture, the greater is the proportion of crystals that have separated by cleavage.

A further important characteristic of such fractures is the 'shear lip' region on the edges of the fracture, as can be seen in Figs. 2.7 and 2.8. Such regions have a sharp serrated edge and have the appearance characteristic of shear fracture on planes at 45° to the applied tensile stress. The size of the shear lip depends on the general brittleness of the fracture or more precisely on the state of stress, whether predominantly plane stress or predominantly plane strain (see p. 86), existing through the thickness under the specific conditions. In some cases the shear lip may be practically non-existent, i.e. a fully flat fracture indicating extreme brittleness, whereas in other cases a fully shear fracture may occur and in such cases the whole of the fracture is slanted. In most cases the fracture surface is composed of both slanted and flat regions.

The process of formation of a brittle fracture in a mild steel plate loaded in tension, having a notch in one edge, would appear to be as follows: As the load is increased, plastic deformation occurs locally at the root of the notch and eventually a small crack develops at the mid thickness. This initial crack extends to form a fibrous 'thumbnail' (see Fig. 2.8), the size of which will vary according to the test conditions, being very small or virtually non-existent in very brittle materials.

Once the initial crack has formed and provided that the load continues to increase, crack propagation occurs by either of two mechanisms. One mechanism is that of gross shear deformation, which requires considerable work to be done by the external forces in order to extend the crack, and

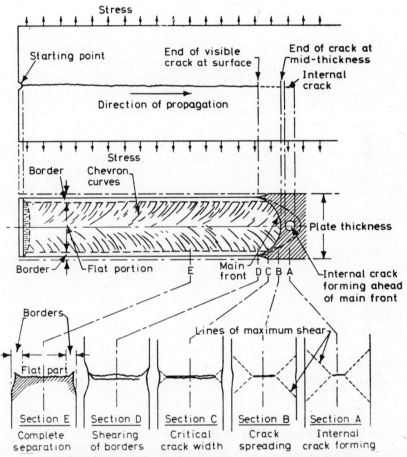

Fig. 2.8. *Stages in the development of a progressing brittle fracture*

considerable plastic deformation is evident from the fracture surface. Alternatively, an entirely different mechanism may intervene at some stage in the development of the initial crack. At some distance beyond the tip of the crack, in the centre of the plate, where the stress system is highly triaxial, i.e. fully plane strain, a group of crystals fractures by cleavage forming a disc shaped crack. This internal crack rapidly grows and in so doing produces the necessary conditions for other similar internal cracks to be developed.

These disc-shaped internal cracks expand and coalesce forming the curved crack front as shown in Fig. 2.8 which propagates with extreme rapidity and with little absorption of energy until arrested or a complete fracture ensues.

Such a fracture, which apparently is self-propagating, since it propagates without necessity of any increase in external load, is described as being 'unstable'.

2.2.2. Energy Considerations

The energy considerations for this type of fracture were first studied by Griffith,[6] who by comparison of the elastic energy released by an extension of a crack with the work done against the resistance of the material in the same extension, was able to determine whether the fracture process would be stable or unstable. Stable fracture is a process in which work must be done by the external forces in order to extend the crack. A simple example of this is tearing a piece of cloth from one edge by a steady pull. Stable fracture is controllable in that the process can be stopped merely by ceasing to pull. Unstable fracture on the other hand, occurs under the action of the elastic energy, stored in the body itself, which is released during the fracture process. An example of this is the bursting of an elastically stressed diaphragm such as a drumhead. Once the drum is punctured the fracture progresses uncontrollably, the driving force for crack extension being the elastic energy initially stored in the diaphragm. Propagation thus occurs without the need for further work by external forces.

The fracture mechanics approach to fracture instability is one in which the criterion for propagation of a crack in a body can be considered in terms of the rates of change, with respect to crack extension, of the various energy components involved in the energy balance of the process. Crack propagation may occur if the amount of energy which can be supplied to the crack tip during an incremental crack extension is greater than or equal to the energy which would be absorbed at the crack tip during the incremental extension of the crack. The five energy components involved in a crack extension process are:

1. Strain energy.
2. Energy supply to the body by external work.
3. Kinetic energy.
4. Surface energy required to form the new crack surfaces.
5. The energy required to develop the plastic deformation at the crack tip.

For materials which exhibit some ductility the surface energy component is exceedingly small compared to the other energy components and can be neglected.

From the energy balance it can be shown that the energy release rate is equal to the rate of change of strain energy with respect to the crack area without change in applied load during incremental crack extension, and is essentially a function of the geometry of the body under consideration and of the stress system. The energy release rate is usually equated to the fracture toughness and is regarded as a measure of the resistance offered by the material to the extension of a crack or crack-like defect.

Considerable developments have taken place over the last 10 years with regard to application of the fracture mechanics approach to low stress fracture and reference is made to this approach in Chapter 6. Comprehensive phenomenological descriptions of fracture processes have been given by Tipper[7, 8] and in 'Fracture'[9] and 'Brittle Fracture of Welded Plate'.[10]

References

1. BOYD, G. M., 'Some Observations on the Brittle Fracture Problem', *Welding Research Council (USA) Bulletin*, No 57 (1960)
2. MATTON-SJOBERG, P., 'The mechanisms of Fracture in Impact Tests', *West of Scotland Iron and Steel Inst. Paper*, No 454 (1953)
3. LESSELLS, *Strength and Resistance of Metals*, John Wiley & Sons Inc., New York (1954)
4. BOYD, G. M., Paper No 2 of 'Toughness and Brittleness in Metals', *Institution of Metallurgists*, London (1961)
5. BOYD, G. M., 'The Propagation of Fractures in Mild Steel Plates', *Engineering*, **175**, No 4538 and 4539, 65 and 100 (January 16 and 23, 1953)
6. GRIFFITH, A. A., *Phil. Trans, Royal Society*, A-**221**, 163–8 (1920)
7. TIPPER, C. F., 'The Fracture of Mild Steel Plate', *Admiralty Ship Welding Committee Report*, R3, HMSO (1948)
8. TIPPER, C. F., *The Brittle Fracture Story*, Cambridge University Press (1962)
9. *Fracture*, John Wiley & Sons Inc., New York; Chapman & Hall, London (1959)
10. *Brittle Fracture of Welded Plate*, Prentice-Hall (1967)

CHAPTER 3

ENGINEERING AND METALLURGICAL FACTORS INFLUENCING FRACTURE

Before discussing the factors which tend to favour or inhibit fracturing, there is need to understand the meanings of 'initiation', 'propagation' and 'arrest'.

Consider a wide plate in tension, having a notch at one edge. As the load increases, yielding and work hardening occur locally at the root of the notch and eventually a small crack opens up in the normal fibrous manner (see Chapter 2). Up to this point, the process is known as initiation.

After the crack has formed, and if the load continues to increase, propagation ensues and may take either of two forms. In the first of these, the crack continues to extend as a stable shear fracture, with considerable absorption of energy, and requiring an equivalent input of work. In the second alternative, it progresses in an unstable manner as described in Section 2.2. Either of these processes is known as 'propagation'. The stopping of a fracture within a member is known as arrest.

A rapid, unstable fracture need not necessarily be entirely of the cleavage type because some of the crystals may be so orientated that they break more readily by shearing accompanied by distortion. Also, the 'bridges' between adjacent internal cleavage cracks may break by shearing. In such cases we have essentially brittle unstable fractures which are formed partly by cleavage and partly by shearing.

The factors which influence the initiation, propagation and arrest of fractures may be roughly divided into 'engineering' factors and 'metallurgical' factors, although usually both are intermixed. The engineering factors comprise mainly those which can be controlled by the designer or which are imposed by the operating conditions and environment, while the metallurgical factors are those which are inherent in the material whether as initially supplied or as changed by fabricating processes, operating conditions and environment.

3.1. ENGINEERING FACTORS

3.1.1. Stress Concentration and Notch Effects

Any change in the cross-section of a member subjected to load has the effect of disturbing the simple assumed nominal stress distribution as calculated by designers, resulting in local concentrations of stress and strain. Any such change may be described as a notch effect. It may, however, range in severity from a mild concentration, caused by a gradual change, to a very severe concentration at the root of a sharp notch. The most severe concentration occurs at the root of a natural crack. As any such concentration favours the initiation of a crack, particularly under fatigue conditions, the engineer's first concern should be to avoid, as far as possible, any severe form of discontinuity or notch, whether as a design feature or accidental. Accidental notches include weld defects (cracks, inclusions, undercutting, porosity, etc) as well as dents, chisel marks and the like.

3.1.2. Temperature

Probably the most important environmental factor is the temperature at which the structure must operate. Experience shows that brittle fractures are liable to be more frequent and more extensive the lower the temperature. This effect is not due to stresses arising from temperature gradients, but to differences in the behaviour of the material itself resulting from the prevailing temperature. In some steels conditions may exist where a difference of a few degrees, even within the normal range of atmospheric temperatures, may determine the difference between ductile and brittle behaviour. The choice of steels for various expected temperatures will be discussed more fully in Chapter 7. More detailed information on the effects of temperature is given by Tipper.[1]

3.1.3. Speed of Loading and Impact

It is well established that steel structures which behave quite normally under static or slowly applied loads may behave in a brittle manner when subjected to sudden applications of load such as shock or impact. This is partly due to the fact that stresses set up by shock waves may be very high (see Timoshenko[2]) and partly to more recondite effects influenced by the properties of the material. In particular, suddenly applied loads can greatly raise the yield point momentarily, increasing the liability to cleavage.[3]

It follows that the effects of sudden loading cannot be adequately counteracted just by making an 'impact allowance' in the form of a reduction in design stress. Such an allowance is effective only to the extent that it provides some margin to accommodate the stress waves, but it is also necessary to consider how the material itself responds to high strain rates and to select a sufficiently tough steel.

3.1.4. Massiveness

There is a well established tendency for brittle behaviour to be more probable in massive than in light structures, for a given stress and temperature level. This again is partly due to stress conditions and partly to metallurgical effects. Thick sections are more likely to include regions in which there are 'triaxial' tensile stresses. Moreover, in thick sections it is more difficult to ensure metallurgical uniformity, because of normal segregation and the fact that the inner layers cool more slowly than the outer. In the design and fabrication of heavy structures, therefore, it is even more necessary to avoid notches and to ensure that the overall notch ductility of the steel is adequate.

3.1.5. Work Hardening

Frequently, the fabrication processes involve local plastic straining of the material, for example by cold bending, hammering, chipping or shearing. This causes local work hardening of the steel and can lead to embrittlement due to strain ageing effects.[4] Strain ageing increases the susceptibility to brittle fracture at higher temperatures. The harmful effects of strain ageing are enhanced by the degree of cold work and by an increase in the ageing temperature. In soft mild steels strain ageing effects resulting from normal fabrication processes may sometimes be tolerable but in the higher tensile steels they are usually more serious and potentially dangerous from the brittle fracture viewpoint. Even in ordinary steels, the possibilities of brittle fracture being initiated at such work hardened parts cannot be ignored[5] and could be serious in particular circumstances which promote strain ageing such as 'hot dip' galvanising of 'as rolled', cold bent or formed sections.

3.1.6. Chemical Environments

It has been mentioned (Chapter 2) that certain chemical environments, in particular alkaline solutions, may give rise to stress corrosion cracking when the steel so exposed is under stress for prolonged periods, especially if it has been subjected to plastic strain.[6] Marine and corrosive chemical environments have also caused corrosion fatigue cracking of mild and low alloy steels, at levels of applied cyclic stress as low as ± 2 ton/in^2 (3·1 kg/mm^2). Structures intended to sustain such conditions require special care and expert knowledge in their design and in the choice of materials, protective coatings, etc. It is to be noted that high concentrations of the chemical may occur locally at interstices of the structure, such as overlaps or laminations, due to local evaporation of the solvent.[6, 7]

3.1.7. Preloading and Proof Loading

A detailed consideration of this factor is presented in Chapter 5, Section 5.3.

3.2. METALLURGICAL FACTORS

The main factors that can be controlled by the manufacturer of the steel or influenced by the designer in choosing the materials, are the following:

1. *Cleavage* seems to be favoured by large grain size, which may be found in some types of steel either as a result of unsuitable heat treatment or due to massiveness of the section, as in forgings.
2. *Brittleness* is encouraged by excessive amounts of non-metallic elements such as carbon, nitrogen, oxygen, hydrogen, sulphur and phosphorus being present in the steel. Silicon, however, is innocuous in the amounts usually found in structural steel. On the other hand most of the ordinary metallic alloying elements such as manganese, nickel, chromium and

vanadium tend to be beneficial, provided that the quantities and heat treatments are correctly chosen. Some metallic elements, such as arsenic and tin, may be detrimental.

3. *Non-metallic inclusions* in the steel may be detrimental, depending on their size, shape and distribution in relation to the applied stress. Gross pockets of non-metallic matter constitute defects liable to originate fracture.

4. *Laminations* (i.e. separation of the metal into layers parallel to the surface) do not generally lead to brittle fractures, but they may cause trouble in welding and flame cutting. The presence of both laminations and clusters of smaller inclusions can form planes of weakness and increase the susceptibility to failure in the through-the-thickness direction. They may also form interstices in which active corrosion can occur.

5. *Heat treatments* strongly influence the properties of steel including those applied as a matter of routine during production of the steel. Some heat treatments, such as normalising, quenching and tempering, and 'stress relieving', are usually beneficial from the brittle fracture viewpoint, but others such as annealing may be detrimental. The choice of heat treatment is a matter for experts.

6. *Fully killed steels*, particularly when grain-refined, are generally tougher than semi-killed steels, and these in turn are generally tougher than 'rimmed' steels. This, however, is not invariably so, and there is considerable overlapping.

7. *Work hardening* may be applied to steel during manufacture, and fabrication, and this can be detrimental.

8. *Surface defects*, such as pitting, constitute stress concentrations and are therefore undesirable.

3.2.1. Effects of Welding

Experience has shown that a large proportion of the brittle fractures that have occurred in service have originated from welds or their vicinity.

When a fusion welding process is adopted an intense source of heat is applied to the weld preparation so as to raise the material locally to melting point. Normally, molten filler metal is added to fill the weld preparation and this mixes with any melted parent metal. As the region heated is usually small in comparison with the size of plate, the rate of cooling is rapid, both in the weld metal and in the heat affected zone (HAZ), because of the relatively efficient conduction of heat from the weld into the neighbouring colder material. Thus, the weld metal may be likened to a small chill casting surrounded by a band of material which is first rapidly heated and then rapidly cooled, the peak temperature decreasing steeply across the HAZ.

The following general consequences may directly result:

1. Introduction of defects not present in the parent metal.
2. Modification of the material adjacent to defects, so that its notch ductility is locally diminished.

3. A general reduction in the notch ductility of the heat affected zone.
4. Introduction of weld metal having a different notch ductility from that of the parent metal.
5. Introduction of both thermal and residual stresses.

It is impossible to eliminate all forms of defect from a practical engineering structure but great importance attaches to reducing the number and size of the defects to the practical minimum.

Welding produces tensile residual stresses of yield point magnitude in the vicinity of the weld, which stresses increase the likelihood of brittle fracture if the material is susceptible to it, even in the absence of external loads. Spontaneous brittle fractures have occurred due to welding stresses alone, for example, during fabrication.

The metallurgical effects of the plastic straining and thermal cycles, due to welding, locally reduce the notch ductility of the parent metal as compared with unaffected material. Moreover, the weld metal may have a different inherent notch ductility because of its different composition and metallurgical structure.

In carbon manganese steels the effect of 'stress relief' heat treatment is not only to relieve residual stresses across any defect but also to restore the notch ductility of the regions, adjacent to the defect, damaged by strain ageing. It should be noted that while stress relief is generally beneficial for carbon manganese steels, it may actually increase the embrittlement adjacent to defects in certain alloy steels, e.g. certain steels containing vanadium, and when using such steels, metallurgical advice should be sought.

3.2.2. Heat Affected Zone Defects

3.2.2.1. *Grain Growth*

In the HAZ, immediately adjacent to the fusion boundary, grain growth will normally occur during welding and this may reduce the notch ductility. In extreme cases it may be necessary to normalise in order to restore the desired properties, for example, when high heat inputs are used as in electro-slag welding. However, the increased strength of the HAZ region probably reduces the risk of fracture initiating or propagating there, unless notch ductility is drastically reduced. It is a matter of general experience that in very few cases of brittle fracture in service has there been any tendency for the fracture to run along a welded joint, except when the weld has been grossly defective (see Chapter 1).

3.2.2.2. *Burning and Hot Tearing*

The foregoing behaviour may be modified, however, if there is a drastic deterioration in HAZ notch ductility. In certain cases, the heat of welding may cause spreading of liquified sulphide eutectic films around grain boundaries. The notch ductility is reduced when these sulphides solidify as brittle films and moreover micro-cracks may be formed if the thermal strains pull the grains apart while the sulphide films are still liquid. This problem occurs where the sulphur level is above about 0·03% and the manganese to sulphur ratio is less than about 20:1. It is seldom encountered with carbon levels less than 0·15%, even with higher sulphur levels, but if the carbon level is increased, the required manganese to sulphur ratio necessary to avoid the trouble must also increase. Hot tearing is more likely to occur in welding processes characterised by a high heat input, such as submerged arc welding, oxyacetylene welding and electro-slag welding.

The damage produced by such hot tearing and burning cannot be repaired by post weld heat treatment and its avoidance depends upon the selection of material with a sufficiently low impurity content, for both the parent metal and the filler metal.

3.2.2.3. *Heat Affected Zone Hydrogen Cracking*

The most common HAZ defects are those resulting from the presence of hydrogen in the weld. Hydrogen is absorbed into the weld pool as a result of the breakdown of hydrogen-containing compounds in the heat of the arc to produce hydrogen in atomic form, which dissolves in the molten weld metal. Once in the weld, it is relatively mobile and diffuses into the HAZ. If the cooling rate in the HAZ is fast enough to produce hard metallurgical structures, spontaneous cracking can then occur under the influence of the residual stresses. The cracking may be very extensive, but at the same time difficult to detect, since the cracks often follow the fusion boundary very closely and, if they emerge at the surface of the plate, do so at the root of the weld or at the edge of the weld reinforcement. This form of cracking has been variously called underbead cracking, cold cracking, hydrogen cracking and delayed cracking.

The risk of this type of cracking depends on the chemical composition and thickness of the parent material, the nature of the joint and the restraint provided by the welded assembly as well as on the energy input and hydrogen potential of the welding process. It may be avoided by raising the preheat and/or interpass temperature by means of post-weld heat treatment; by raising the energy input of the welding process; by choosing a process and consumables giving a low weld hydrogen content and by specifying a steel not susceptible to the problem under the conditions envisaged in welding. The latter remedy is the most effective for reasons which have been explained in detail elsewhere.[8, 9, 10]

To sum up, the avoidance of this type of cracking depends on detailed observance of the correct welding procedure in relation to joint geometry and the actual composition of the steel. These factors make it impossible to lay down precise procedures for general use.

For general guidance on the welding of BS 968:1962 (now incorporated in BS 4360:1968) and similar higher-strength steels the reader is referred to BS 2642:1965. This emphasises that where preheat is necessary to avoid hydrogen cracking, it will generally be necessary to carry out trials with several different welding procedures to establish those which are most satisfactory for the particular conditions.

3.2.3. Weld Metal Defects

Weld metal may contain crack-like defects either of metallurgical origin or due to inadequate skill on the part of the operator. Generally speaking, a high sulphur and phosphorus level, derived either from the parent material or from contamination of the weld, may lead to cracking during solidification, or to poor notch ductility. It is generally found that basic coated electrodes (Class E.6XX) produce fewer defects and better toughness than rutile coated electrodes (Classes E.2XX and E.3XX). However, welds in mild steel show a remarkable tolerance for defects, probably due at least in part to the fact that the strength of the weld metal is greater than that of the parent plate, so that if service loads are applied to the weld, the strain taking place across imperfections is relatively small because of the higher comparative strength of the material surrounding them. However, it should be recognised that this argument only holds when the strength of the weld metal is considerably greater than that of the parent plate. Thus a defect in a mild steel weld metal of yield strength 30 ton/in^2 (46 kg/mm^2) might well have no appreciable effect on the fracture behaviour of mild steel parent plate having a yield strength of 15 ton/in^2 (23 kg/mm^2). On the other hand it might constitute a path of relatively easy fracture when applied to plate of, say, 28 ton/in^2 (44 kg/mm^2) yield strength. The matter of notch ductility requirements for weld metal is discussed in Chapter 7.

3.2.4. Effects of Flame Cutting

In the same way as hardened heat affected zones are produced by welding, such regions also occur adjacent to flame cut edges. Thus, underbead cracking of the type described above can also occur as a result of flame cutting. It is generally agreed to be bad practice to weld directly on to a flame cut surface unless the latter is fully absorbed in the weld. In cases where very hard heat affected zones are formed by flame cutting, removal of the hardened region by machining or grinding is sometimes required. The most appropriate procedure, however, is to prevent the formation of hardened regions and hence cracks, by either pre-heating or post heating the flame cut regions.

3.2.5. Inspection of Welds

Experience of service failures by brittle fracture has shown that initiation of fracture frequently occurs at some form of welding defect. Whilst it is unrealistic to suggest that welded fabrications can be completed entirely free of all defects, non-destructive inspection of welds can be used to exclude defects of a size and nature likely to initiate brittle fracture. Inspection is no substitute for the correct choice of materials and welding procedures but is a necessary part of overall precautions. When the correct materials have been chosen for the particular service conditions to avoid either initiation or propagation of brittle fractures there will be some tolerance for weld defects, but the actual size and type of defect which can be tolerated can only be decided in the knowledge of the particular materials and operating conditions.[11]

Non-destructive examination of welds can be carried out by visual observation, by dye penetrant techniques, by magnetic particle techniques, by radiography or by ultrasonics.[11] Each of these techniques can only be expected to detect certain forms of defect in certain orientations and none of them can be relied upon to detect all forms of defect. The visual dye penetrant, and magnetic particle techniques can only detect cracks at or near to the surface. Radiography and ultrasonics can be used to detect internal weld defects, although some interpretive judgement is required in assessing the type and significance of defects so revealed. A decision on the degree of non-destructive examination after welding should be taken at the design and material selection stage so that the fabricator is aware of the standards to which he has to work.

References

1. TIPPER, C. F., *The Brittle Fracture Story*, Cambridge University Press (1962)
2. TIMOSHENKO, *Theory of Elasticity*, McGraw-Hill (1934)
3. TAYLOR, D. B. C., *Navy Department Advisory Committee on Structural Steel Report*, No P6, HMSO (1965)
4. TIPPER, C. F., 'Materials damage attributable to welding—a commentary', *British Welding Journal*, 13, 461–466 (1966)
5. LAMIRAL, G. and LECLER, R., 'La réalisation à Chinon des caissons de Réacteurs EDF1 et EDF2', *Soudage et Techniques Connexes*, 16, No 11/12 (November/December, 1962)
6. EVANS, U. R., *The Corrosion and Oxidation of Metals*, Edward Arnold Publishers, London (1960)
7. SCHREIR, L. L., *Corrosion, Vol 1, Corrosion of Metals and Alloys*, Geo Newnes Ltd., London (1965)
8. BURDEKIN, F. M., *British Welding Journal*, 14, No 2 (1967)
9. BAKER, R. G., *BWRA Bulletin*, 8 (July, 1967)
10. WATKINSON, F. and BAKER, R. G., *British Welding Journal*, 14, No 11 (1967)
11. *Non-destructive methods for the examination of welds*, BWRA Memorandum

CHAPTER 4

METHODS OF TESTING FOR NOTCH DUCTILITY

It will be evident from the previous chapters that metals are capable of many different responses to loading. The initiation, propagation and arrest of fractures are governed by an interplay of many varying factors, some mechanical and some metallurgical, but it is not yet clearly understood what decides between the alternative possible responses in any given case.

Though it would indeed be convenient if some single measurable property of a metal existed whereby the propensity to brittle fracture in a structure could be confidently predicted, no such single property has been discovered for structural steels. For ultra high strength steels there is now considerable evidence that fracture toughness can be assessed by the linear elastic fracture mechanics plane strain toughness parameter, K_{Ic}.[1] It is not, however, possible at present to obtain valid measurements of this parameter for lower strength steels in commonly used thicknesses under slow loading conditions, except at temperatures at which the notch ductility of such steels is inherently low. In the absence of a generally agreed measure of notch ductility for widespread use in the assessment of structural steels, this chapter will be devoted to summarising the nature and the implications of the various tests that can be used for ascertaining separately the various responses to types of loading and levels of temperature that have influence on brittle fracture.

Most of the tests for notch toughness have been developed for plates and are not always applicable to sections. The properties of the latter are often inferior to those of plates and this fact has to be recognised and allowed for.

The normal tensile test gives no indication of the tendency to brittle fracture and will not therefore be referred to further.

4.1. PENDULUM IMPACT TESTS ON SMALL SPECIMENS

The principle of these tests is that the specimen is positioned across the lowest point in the path of a striker mounted on the end of a pendulum. The striker, having been initially lifted to a certain height and then released, swings against the specimen and breaks it. The striker, continuing its swing, then rises on the other side of the specimen to a height which is less than the initial height, so that the difference between the two heights multiplied by the mass of the striker corresponds with the amount of energy absorbed in producing the fracture. The appearance of the fracture surfaces (the percentage of crystallinity) and the distortion of the specimens provide additional clues for assessing the brittleness of the fractures.

Such tests are usually carried out on a series of specimens at different controlled temperatures, so that the effect of temperature on the other variables can be observed.

Two types of machine have commonly been used for this. In the Izod machine, the specimen is gripped in vice jaws so as to project into the path of the striker as a vertical cantilever. The fact that the vice jaws as well as the specimen itself have to be brought to and kept at the required temperature renders temperature control difficult, for which reason this arrangement is seldom used nowadays and the Charpy machine is preferred.

Fig. 4.1. *Charpy machine (By courtesy of W. & T. Avery Ltd.)*

In the Charpy machine illustrated in Fig. 4.1 the specimen is a horizontal beam spanning across the path of the striker. The procedure for carrying out the test is covered by British Standard BS131 part 2: 1959. Only the specimen itself needs to be brought to the required temperature, since it has merely to be laid in position and can be broken before the temperature has had time to change significantly. Some machines have been developed so as to be convertible from Izod to Charpy and vice versa.

In both types of machine the specimen normally consists of a bar of 10 mm square cross-section (though in the Izod machine it is sometimes cylindrical) having a notch at the position of maximum bending moment, i.e. at the surface of the vice jaws in the Izod machine and at the centre of the span in the Charpy. The shape and dimensions of the notch vary considerably in different specifications. The commonest type of notch in use at present is the Charpy V-notch shown in Fig. 4.2(a), namely a 45° notch, 2 mm deep with a 0·25 mm root radius (BS.131: Part 2:1959) but there are also the Charpy Keyhole type Fig. 4.2(b) and the Mesnager type Fig. 4.2(c).[2]

In the Schnadt variation of the Charpy test a hardened round pin is inserted through a hole near the compression side of the specimen (Fig. 4.2(d)) with

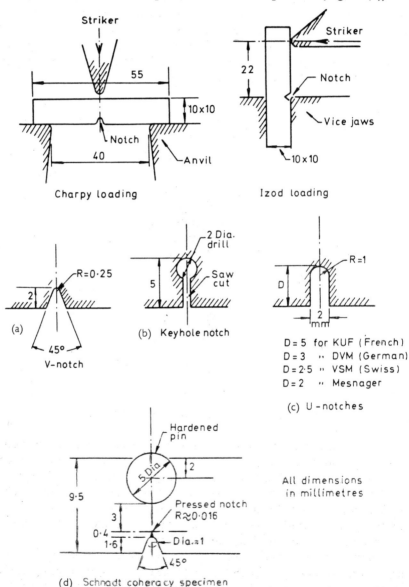

Fig. 4.2. *Notched specimens for impact testing. (a) Charpy V-notch; (b) Charpy keyhole; (c) Mesnager tests; (d) Schnadt coheracy specimen*

the object of reducing extraneous distortions. The striker impinges on this pin instead of directly on the surface of the specimen, so that little plastic deformation occurs in the compression half of the latter. The acuity of the notch and also the rate of straining can be varied.[3]

In the Hounsfield impact test, very small round specimens are held in one pendulum and struck by another,[4] so that the reaction on the foundations is reduced.

In all such forms of test the temperature of the specimen is controlled, usually by immersing it in a bath of liquid at the required temperature. Above 0° C warm water is commonly used, at 0° C water with melting ice and at lower temperatures other liquids such as alcohol or glycol solutions

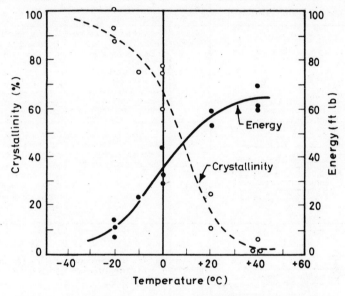

Fig. 4.3. *Scatter diagram of typical results of Charpy V-notch tests*

cooled by dry ice. To produce 'transition curves' for a given sample of steel, several specimens are prepared and groups of these are tested at intervals of temperature, the results being plotted against temperature to form a scatter diagram through which a curve is drawn. In all notched tests a considerable amount of scatter is to be expected, particularly in the transition range, as exemplified in Fig. 4.3.[5] The energy value at a given temperature is derived from the curve as described, or by taking the average of several (preferably not less than three) tests made at the chosen temperature.

The transition of any given steel from tough to brittle behaviour is affected by the type of test and by the geometry of the specimen. Several criteria are frequently derived from the tests, such as the following:

1. The energy absorbed in fracturing the specimen at some arbitrary temperature (such as 0° C).

2. The temperature at which the energy absorption at fracture reaches some arbitrary proportion (such as 50%), of its maximum value.
3. The temperature corresponding to the point of inflection in the energy versus temperature curve, i.e. where the slope of the curve is steepest.
4. The temperature at which the fracture shows some arbitrary percentage of crystallinity.

4.2. TESTS ON SPECIMENS OF FULL PLATE THICKNESS

The pendulum impact tests described above are popular because the specimens, being small, are easy and cheap to prepare and test in large numbers,

Particulars of specimen	Method of load	Criteria for assessing transition temperature	Remarks
Tipper notched tensile 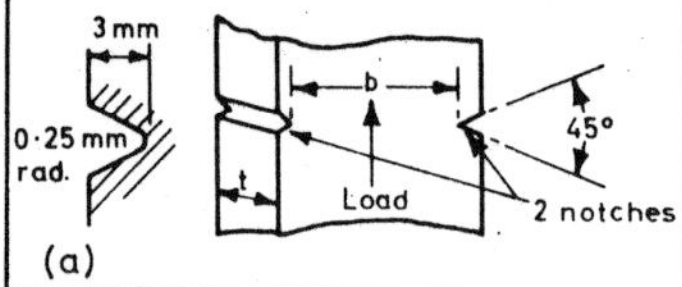 3 mm, 0·25 mm rad., Load, b, 45°, 2 notches (a)	Static tension	1. Fracture appearance 2. Ductility— a) Extension over notch b) Reduction in thickness 3. Work done when record of load/extension available	Uniform rectangular strips of full plate thickness (unless limited by capacity of testing machine). Width 'b' greater than thickness 't': preferably b = 2·5 t. Length to suit grips.
Robertson 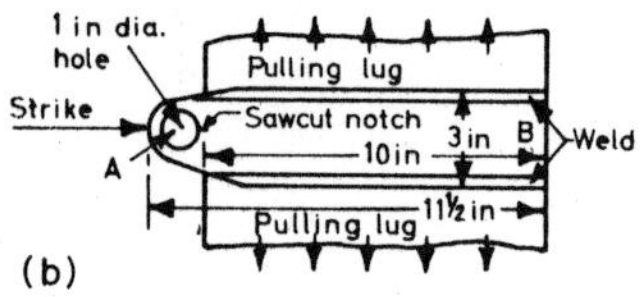 1 in dia. hole, Pulling lug, Strike, Sawcut notch, 10in, 3in B, Weld, A, Pulling lug, 11½in (b)	Static tension with initiation by impact	1. Temperature at which crack stops 2. Stress at arrest temperature	Temperature gradient provided by liquid nitrogen at 'A' and gas flame at 'B.' Tests are carried out at various transverse stress levels
Van der Veen 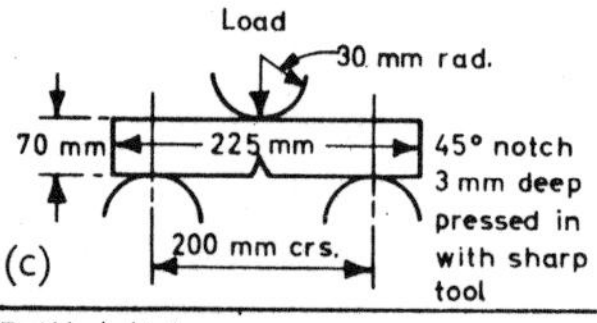 Load, 30 mm rad., 70 mm, 225 mm, 45° notch 3 mm deep pressed in with sharp tool, 200 mm crs. (c)	Static bending	1. Fracture appearance 2. Load/deflection curve	Full thickness of plate used
Pellini bulge 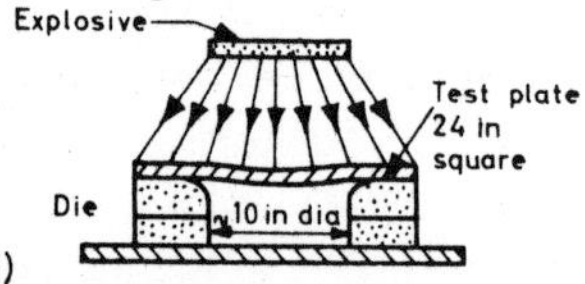 Explosive, Test plate 24 in square, Die, 10 in dia (d)	Explosion	Character of fracture	A notch is ground in a short bead of brittle weld deposited at the centre of the specimen to initiate fracture
Pellini drop weight 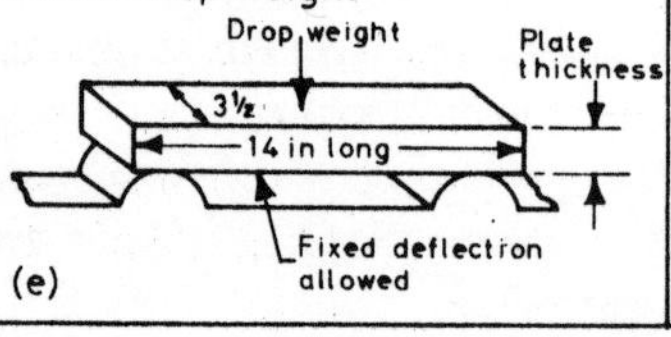 Drop weight, Plate thickness, 3½, 14 in long, Fixed deflection allowed (e)	Impact bending	Temperature above which fracture does not occur	A notch is ground in a short longitudinal bead of brittle weld deposited on the tension surface to initiate fracture. Full plate thickness up to and including 1 in.

Fig. 4.4. *Five tests on specimens of full plate thickness (By courtesy of Royal Institution of Naval Architects)*

yielding results which can be treated statistically, whether for quality control in routine production or, for instance, in the investigation of casualty material. However, in such tests it is not easy to distinguish the relative importance of fracture initiation and fracture propagation, both being involved. Moreover they cannot reveal 'size effects' since the specimens are of uniform size. For these reasons it is virtually impossible by means of such tests to obtain direct information on how steel is likely to behave in an actual plate or structural part. Accordingly, other types of test using the full thickness of the material have been developed. Five of these are sketched at (a) to (e) in Fig. 4.4.[6]

4.2.1. Tipper Notched Tensile Test

The notched tensile test due to Tipper[7] is performed on specimens having the form sketched in Fig. 4.4(a), i.e. uniform rectangular strips of full plate thickness (unless limited by the capacity of the testing machine) but in any case preferably having a width not less than $2\frac{1}{2}$ times the thickness. Specimens of steel which show normal ductility in the ordinary tensile test tend to break in a brittle manner if they are notched as shown. The notches make it possible to achieve cleavage fractures at normal atmospheric temperatures and the shape of the notch can be varied in order to study the effect of notch acuity. If this test is repeated at a series of different temperatures, the transition temperature, or range, can be assessed from the proportion of crystalline texture observed in the fractured surfaces. The transition temperature can also be determined from measurements of the extensions of the test pieces at fracture, the reductions in thickness at fracture or from load-extension diagrams that show the energy to fracture. Over the transition range, all these quantities show marked reductions as the appearance of the fracture changes from fibrous to crystalline.

Like all notched bar tests, the Tipper notch-tensile test gives results subject to scatter arising from the conjunction of such variables as inconsistencies of the material and the inherent uncertainty as to whether failure may occur by shear or by cleavage. This adds to the difficulty of assessing a particular material on insufficient information, but the notched tensile test is simple and practical. Its indications have been shown to correlate with service behaviour.[6, 7] Some plots of Tipper test results are shown in Fig. 4.5(c). The test has been extensively used in investigations, but up to now it has not been widely adopted in specifications.

4.2.2. Robertson Test

This test, devised by T. S. Robertson at the Naval Construction Research Establishment, Rosyth, determines a 'crack arrest' temperature (CAT). The object of the Crack Arresting test is to determine threshold conditions of stress and temperature for propagation of brittle fracture in steel plate material. An article in the British Welding Journal[8] gives a full description of the development of the test and procedure.

The specimen used, which may be up to 20 in (510 mm) in length, is flame

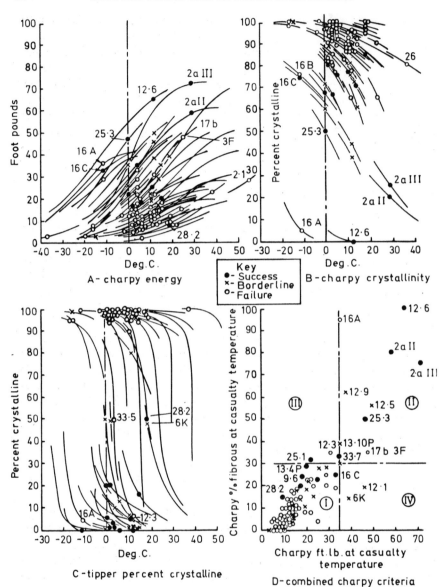

Fig. 4.5. *Tests on casualty material (By courtesy of Royal Institution of Naval Architects)*

cut from the plate and is welded into a test assembly which is held in a specially designed testing machine (Fig. 4.4(b)). The specimen is made so that crack initiation can be actuated from the tip of a jeweller's saw-cut at one end while the specimen is loaded to a chosen level of stress and cooled or heated to give a predetermined temperature gradient along the intended crack path.

The testing machine which applies the load is provided with means for controlling the alignment of the test piece relative to the loading axis. To facilitate even loading, and to relax welding stresses, the specimen is flanked by spacers, which are welded to both specimen and loading ends. These spacers yield so that the loading on the specimen is redistributed while the stress in the specimen remains within the elastic limit. After yielding the spacers it is a simple matter to get a uniform stress along both sides of the specimen in the crack path by the use of the alignment control and readings from attached strain gauges.

The test procedure requires a known temperature distribution to be set up along the crack path, having a gradient if it is intended to carry out a simple assessment of temperature at which a ductile lip appears, or having a constant temperature (isothermal) region if the object is to determine whether or not the crack will arrest after entering the region of constant temperature after leaving the gradient zone. In either case the zone around the notch is generally cooled well below ambient temperature by evaporating liquid nitrogen syphoned to the area. In both the gradient and isothermal tests it may be necessary to heat or cool the specimen along the length to get the required temperature distribution. It is usually possible to stabilise the temperature condition for a sufficient time to allow the test to be carried out without manipulation of controls during the actual test.

The test is carried out after the required load has been applied and the temperature conditions have been established. Fracture is initiated by a sudden magnification of the strain at the tip of the jeweller's saw-cut, brought about by the impact of an explosively driven bolt striking the rounded end of a projecting nose, or alternatively, lodging in a small hole bisected by the saw-cut.

The key factors in assessing the result of the test are: the extent to which the crack runs along the temperature gradient, in the case of a gradient test; or whether it arrests, or arrests and restarts in the constant temperature zone in the case of an isothermal test, as well as the nature of the fracture appearance.

Larger machines, which are used only for isothermal tests, have been developed with radically different features, capable of applying much greater loads and accommodating much wider specimens. Two such machines, one of 1 200 ton (1 220 000 kg) capacity at NCRE Dunfermline and one of 4 000 ton (4 064 000 kg) capacity at UKAEA Culcheth, utilise the same principle but differ in detailed design and can test plates having widths up to 6 ft (1·83 m) and 8 ft (2·44 m) respectively. The larger machines use different specimens and assembly methods. They are mainly employed for research purposes on thick material and can be adapted to test structural connections. Detailed descriptions of these machines are given elsewhere.[9–12]

4.2.3. Van der Veen Test

In the Van der Veen slow notched bend test[13] the specimen is loaded by static 3-point bending as shown in Fig. 4.4(c). The notch is made by pressing with a sharp knife-edge. The two criteria are (1) the temperature at which the fibrous fracture zone below the notch measures 32 mm and (2) the temperature at which the deflection under maximum load exceeds a certain amount. The test, which relies primarily on fracture appearance, has been extensively used in investigations and for quality control, but has not been widely adopted in specifications.

4.2.4. Wells–BWRA Wide Plate Test

In this test the specimen is a plate 3 ft (915 mm) square, made up of two halves which have their contiguous edges cut to V-sections so as to meet along mutually opposed knife edges. An artificial defect is introduced by making sawcuts in these edges at the midpoint in the length of the plate and the two halves are then connected by a longitudinal butt weld, as shown in Fig. 4.6. The complete specimen is then welded to a special test rig as shown in Fig. 4.7. After the specimen has been cooled to the desired temperature, it is loaded in tension parallel to the butt weld.[14-16]

It is found that this form of test demonstrates the transitional effect of temperature and the fact that, for 'as welded' test plates, below a certain temperature which is characteristic of the steel and welding procedures, fractures

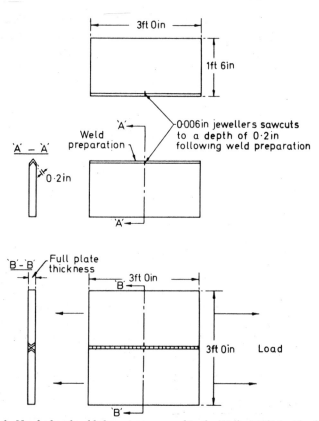

Fig. 4.6. *Notched and welded specimen as used in the Wells–BWRA wide plate test*

Fig. 4.7. *Photograph of Wells wide plate testing machine (By courtesy of The Welding Institute)*

can occur at low applied stresses. Above this temperature the loads have to be sufficient to produce general yielding before fracture initiates.

The test has provided useful information on the significance of residual stress and of defects, and has also demonstrated the benefits of stress relief treatments. Sometimes an alternative cross-welded form of specimen is used to examine risks of fracture along welds. In the cross-welded specimen the notch can be sawn in any desired region of either the weld metal or the heat affected zone. Some authorities use data from this type of wide plate test for material selection to avoid brittle fracture initiation. (See Chapter 7.)

4.2.5. The Explosion Bulge Test

The Pellini explosion bulge test[17] is carried out on a square plate specimen of full thickness as sketched in Fig. 4.4(d). A short run of brittle weld metal is applied at the centre at the bottom surface and a saw-cut notch is made in the bead. The plate is then placed over a die in which there is a circular hole with rounded edges, and a controlled weight of explosive in the form of a disc is detonated at a standard height above it. The criteria are the character of the fracture and the amount of bulging that takes place.

4.2.6. The Drop Weight Test

The Pellini drop weight test[18] shown in Fig. 4.4(e) consists in placing a plate specimen, about 14 in (356 mm) long by $3\frac{1}{2}$ in (89 mm) wide and of specified thickness, on which a short brittle weld bead has been laid, across a standard span and dropping a weight on it from a standard height so as to strike the plate at midspan. The deflection of the specimen is limited by a stop. The criterion adopted is the 'Nil Ductility Temperature' (NDT) meaning the temperature that divides the specimens which fracture through from those which do not. The procedure is covered by ASTM Specification No E-208-63T.

4.2.7. The Drop Weight (or Dynamic) Tear Test

The drop weight tear test[19, 20] also developed originally at the US Naval Research Laboratory (shown in Fig. 4.8), has found extensive use in pipeline applications and in assessing heat affected zones of quenched and tempered steels. In its original form this test consists of a full plate thickness specimen with a notched brittle cast steel bar welded to the tension face with a brittle

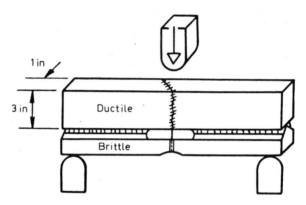

Fig. 4.8. *Drop weight tear test*

weld deposit approximately 4 in (100 mm) long opposite the notch in the cast bar. The rest of the weld joint consists of two root passes made with conventional electrodes normally used for welding the test steels. In its present form a titanium embrittled electron beam weld replaces the cast steel bar. The specimen is orientated so that the plate surfaces form the sides of the specimen, which is bent edgewise by 3-point loading. The testing is carried out in a pendulum machine to record the energy required to produce fracture. Several specimens are tested at temperatures spanning the range of interest. The criteria used in the test are the temperature at which complete shear fracture occurs and the temperature for a particular energy level obtained by correlation with large scale tests.

4.2.8. The Navy Tear Test

In the United States Navy tear test a plate specimen having the dimensions indicated in Fig. 4.9[21] is made to break by a combination of static tension and bending. Load-extension records are made, from which the energy absorbed up to the start of the fracture (pre-crack energy) and that absorbed in its propagation (post crack energy), may be determined. The criterion usually adopted is the temperature at which the fracture appearance changes

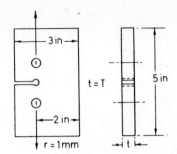

Fig. 4.9. *Navy tear test. Load extension records are made from which the energy absorbed to start the fracture and that to propagate it may be plotted. The criterion usually plotted is fracture appearance which usually coincides with the sudden drop in energy to propagate as in other bend tests*

which, as a rule, coincides with a sudden drop in post crack energy. The pre-crack energy is practically independent of temperature.

4.2.9. The Double Tension Test

This test, which originated in Japan[22] provides an alternative method for determining the crack arrest characteristics of a given steel. Initiation of a brittle crack is obtained by applying tension at low temperature to a notched lug formed on one edge of the main specimen (see Fig. 4.10). The main specimen is independently loaded in tension to the required stress level and held at the required testing temperature. In this way the effects of impact loading at initiation, as used in the Robertson test are avoided. The criterion for the test is whether the fracture propagates across the whole specimen or arrests. Thus by repeating the test at different temperatures and stress levels the crack arrest curve for a steel can be defined. The length of the crack at arrest depends on the temperature and on the level of stress, so that the test can be used to determine the 'fracture toughness' of the steel plate at particular temperatures.

4.2.10. Fracture Mechanics Tests

For ultra high strength materials, fracture toughness values (see Chapter 6, Section 6.3) can be determined by tests on either of several types of test pieces. For valid results to be obtained, fracture must occur under essentially elastic conditions and the test conditions and results must conform with a number of criteria.[1, 23] The fracture mechanics analyses provide a relationship between the external loading conditions, the specimen geometry and the local conditions at the crack tip which describe the stress field in that region. Under truly plane strain conditions, for a given material and test conditions, temperature and loading rate, fracture occurs at a constant critical stress intensity, K_{Ic}, the plane strain fracture toughness.

Several forms of test pieces in common use are shown in Fig. 4.11. For a given thickness, B, in order to ensure plane strain conditions, B should not

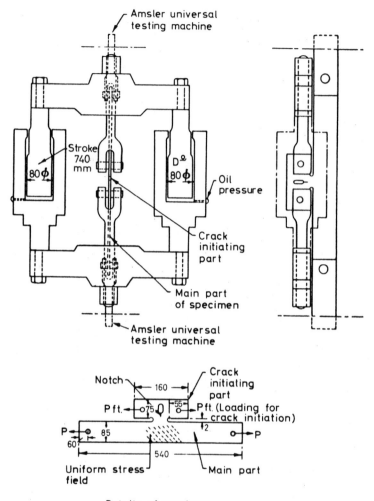

Fig. 4.10. *Double tension test-loading arrangement and specimen*

be less than $2\cdot5(K_{Ic}/\sigma ys)^2$. Consequently, the other dimensions for the test piece must be determined accordingly. Detailed information on the specimen geometry and test procedures for the various types of test piece are given by van der Veen[13] and Kahn and Imbembo.[23]

4.2.11. Interpretation of Test Results

As mentioned above there are several limitations in the use of small scale impact tests. These tests do not reproduce the expected behaviour of material in an actual structure because they rarely take into account size effects, strain rate effects, crack sharpness and effects of welding. Moreover, where energy measurements are recorded they usually involve a contribution from

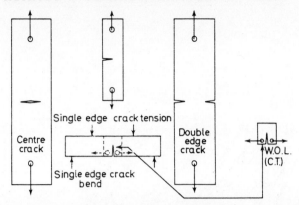

Fig. 4.11. *Types of specimen used in K_{Ic} fracture toughness tests. Note: dimensions of specimens must be determined from the formulae relating them to K_{Ic} and thickness given in References 4.1 and 4.23*

both fracture initiation and fracture propagation. It is appropriate to adopt firm definitions of initiation and propagation of fracture and to consider the various tests discussed above in terms of these definitions. Initiation of fracture is regarded as the stage prior to the first extension of unstable fracture from a pre-existing crack. Propagation of fracture is regarded as the subsequent fracture extension.

Of the various full plate thickness tests described above those which consider percentage crystallinity in the fracture appearance, such as the Tipper test, must be regarded as assessing resistance to fracture propagation. The Robertson test and double tension test are also propagation tests since they assess the propensity of a steel to arrest a running fracture. The Pellini drop weight and explosion bulge tests involve high strain rate loading with initiation of fracture forced to occur in a brittle weld deposit. These tests are therefore propagation tests which assess whether a dynamic crack can continue to propagate under the applied loading conditions. Similarly, the drop weight tear test has a brittle crack starter and is used mainly for the assessment of propagation characteristics. The Navy tear test and the Van der Veen test allow separation of initiation from propagation but again refer to parent material in general rather than to welded joints. The Wells wide plate test is the only full plate thickness test which attempts to assess resistance to fracture initiation taking account of complex effects, including strain ageing, arising from welding.

4.2.12. Correlation Between Tests

Many attempts have been made to find correlations between the results from different forms of test. Fig. 4.12 shows an example, seeking to correlate the Charpy V-notch test with the Pellini explosion bulge test for a range of steels.[6] Other examples of attempted correlation are given later in Section 6.4. It has been established from many such attempts that it is impossible, by means of any simple formula, to convert the transition temperature or other indications obtained from a given test using a given specimen, geometry or

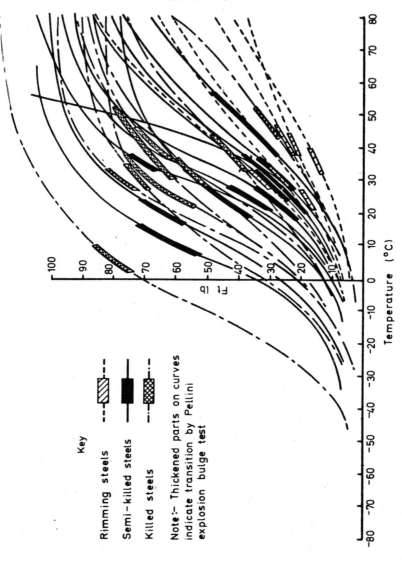

Fig. 4.12. *Attempted correlation between results from Charpy V-notch test (thin curves) and from Pellini explosion bulge test (thickened curves), for three grades of steel (By courtesy of Royal Institution of Naval Architects)*

criterion so as to correspond with the indications from another test under different conditions. Different steels can, therefore, be compared only when the test conditions are identical, and the comparison is only valid for these conditions. (See footnote on page 95.)

This lack of correlation between transition temperatures obtained from different arbitrary tests is not surprising if the tests are not alike in respect of thickness, strain rate, notch acuity and effects of welding.

4.2.13. Tests on Actual Structures

The tests described above, being mainly on small samples, cannot in general fully simulate the conditions in a full scale structure. For this and other reasons, many tests have been made on actual structures and on full scale models of parts of structures. Some of these will be briefly described here, but further details can be found in the references cited.

In the USA, a very thorough investigation of stress distributions on the Liberty Ship *Philip Schuyler* has been described by Vasta.[24] The ship was loaded by known distributions of ballast, and the strains were measured by many electrical and mechanical strain gauges, strategically distributed. Measurements were also made of the deflections of the ship and of local buckling effects.

Also in the USA, extensive investigations were made to determine the residual stresses in actual ships and sub-assemblies, and on the influence of service life on residual stresses.[25, 26]

At about the same time a programme of tests was made at the University of California, first on models and later on full-scale fabricated sections representing several different designs of ships' hatchway corners.[27]

In the United Kingdom, a very extensive series of full scale experiments was carried out on actual ships, mainly with the object of investigating the differences in behaviour of riveted and welded ships. These experiments, which were made under the auspices of the Admiralty Ship Welding Committee have been fully described in a series of reports published by HMSO.[28]

These and other experiments on full scale structures, although inspired by the occurrence of brittle fracture, did not serve to elucidate the phenomenon to any marked extent, but they produced extremely valuable information on stress distributions, particularly at concentrations, and on the loadings sustained by ships at sea. They also showed that there was no significant difference between the flexural rigidities of welded and riveted ships. Some of the hatch corner experiments[27] were made at controlled temperatures, and clearly showed a marked difference in the character of the fractures at different temperatures, in line with the transition effect observed in small scale tests, as described in other parts of this book.

References

1. 'Fracture Toughness Testing and its Applications', *ASTM Special Publication No 381* (1965)
2. TIPPER, C. F., *The Brittle Fracture Story*, Cambridge University Press (1962)

3. SCHNADT, H. M., 'Neue Prüfmethoden von Stahlen und Schweisswerkstoffen für grosse Schweisskonstruktion Teil 1—Grundlagen', *published by the author, Zug, Switzerland*

4. Hounsfield Test, as cited by Tipper in Reference 2

5. *Handbook for Welding Design, Vol 1, 2nd Ed,* The Welding Institute, London, Sir Isaac Pitman & Sons Ltd. (1967)

6. HODGSON, J. and BOYD, G. M., 'Brittle fracture in welded ships', *Trans. Royal Institution of Naval Architects,* **100**, 141–180 (1958)

7. BAKER, J. F., and TIPPER, C. F., 'The value of the Notch Tensile Test', *Proc. Inst. Mech. E.,* **170**, No 1 (October, 1956). Also *US Welding Research Council Bulletin,* No 37

8. 'The Robertson Crack Arrest Test', *British Welding Journal,* 387–394 (August, 1968)

9. ROBERTSON, T. S., 'Experimental Techniques', *Proc. Conference on Properties of Materials at High Rates of Strain, Inst. Mech. E.* (1957)

10. WINDER, B., *Nuclear Engineering,* **7**, 61 (1962)

11. CAGILL, J. M., *J. Mech. Eng.,* **5**, No 1 (1963)

12. ROBERTSON, T. S., 'Brittle Fracture Test', *Inst. Mech. E. Conference, Manchester* (September, 1965)

13. VAN DER VEEN, J. H., 'Development of a Testing Method on Brittle Fracture of Mild Steel Plates', *Symposium on Notch Bar Testing and its Relation to Welded Construction, Institute of Welding* (1953)

14. WELLS, A. A., *Trans. Royal Inst. Naval Architects,* **98**, 296 (1956)

15. WELLS, A. A., *British Welding Journal,* **8**, No 5, 259 (1961)

16. WOODLEY, C. C., BURDEKIN, F. M., and WELLS, A. A., *British Welding Journal,* **11**, No 3, 123 (1964)

17. PUZAK, P. P., ESCHBACHER, E. W., and PELLINI, W. S., 'Initiation and Propagation of Brittle Fracture in Structural Steels', *American Welding Journal,* 561S–581S (December, 1952)

18. *Naval Research Laboratory, Washington (Metallurgy Division),* Reports NRL 5920, March 15 (1963) and NRL 6060, November 5 (1963)

19. PELLINI, W. S., GOODE, R. J., PUZAK, P. P., LANGE, E. A., and HUBER, R. W., *Naval Research Laboratory, Washington,* Report No 6300 (June, 1965)

20. PELLINI, W. S., *Naval Research Laboratory, Washington,* Report No 6713 (April, 1968)

21. KAHN, N. A., and IMBEMBO, E. A., *American Welding Journal,* 84S–96S (February, 1950)

22. YOSHIKI, M. T., KANAZAWA, T., and ITAGAKI, H., 'An Improved Testing Method', *Proc. Third Japan Congress on Testing Materials,* 103 (March, 1960)

23. 'Plain strain crack Toughness Testing of High Strength Metallic Materials', *ASTM Special Technical Publication No 410*

24. VASTA, J., 'Structural Tests on Liberty Ship *Philip Schuyler*', *Trans. American Society of Naval Architects and Marine Engineers,* **55**, 391–431 (1947)

25. DE GARMO, E. P., JONASSEN, F., and MERIAM, J. L., *American Welding Journal,* (June, August, September and October, 1946)

26. FFIELD, P., *American Welding Journal* (November, 1946)

27. DE GARMO, E. P., *American Welding Journal* (February, 1948)

28. *Admiralty Ship Welding Committee Reports,* HMSO, R1 (1946), R2 (1948) and R3 to R12 inclusive, 1953/4

CHAPTER 5

DESIGN CONSIDERATIONS AFFECTING THE CHOICE OF STEEL FOR STRUCTURAL APPLICATIONS

5.1. WORKING STRESSES

One of the primary decisions that have to be made in the design stage is the selection of a 'Design Working Stress'. This decision is frequently controlled by a British Standard or other specification, but the following remarks are intended to guide the designer in forming his own judgement. They are not intended to override the standard specifications, but rather to indicate some of the considerations that underlie them.

At the outset it must be made clear that a design working stress is a purely nominal concept. It is intended to be the basis for fairly simple calculations which have been proved by experience to result in a structure of suitable proportions for its intended purpose. This simple concept, or role, of design stress cannot adequately describe the complicated stress-strain patterns which occur in an actual structure, particularly in the vicinity of discontinuities, notches or changes in section. Nor can it take into account 'residual stresses', i.e. those stresses which exist within the structure independently of the external loading. Such stresses may arise during the manufacture of the steel, due to the actual manufacturing process, such as rolling, extrusion and differential cooling. They also arise from fabrication processes such as cold bending, erection forces, or from the contractions due to welding.

In normal structural design, it is not unusual to regard stress systems as being uniaxial. That is to say that the stress systems are often regarded as either simple tensions, simple compressions, or simple shear. Most actual stress systems, however, are much more complicated. Thus, at any one point in a real structure, all three of the above forms may exist together, but in practical design it is usual to consider only the maximum values, and not the interactions between the three types.

It is important to remember that these simplifications, which are adopted to facilitate the designer's task, can only be justified by successful prior experience. When this is not available, as for example when designing an entirely new type of structure, it behoves the designer to go much more deeply into the details of stress distribution.

It must be remembered that in actual structures, the stresses cannot be directly measured. One can only measure the *strains* (elongations or contractions) and use these to infer the stresses by means of suitable theory. In most practical cases, the relationship between stress and strain is assumed to be linear, i.e. that the behaviour is elastic. This assumption, however, is invalid if yielding occurs anywhere within the region considered. Measurements of variations in strain due to variations in external loading cannot reveal any 'residual' stresses or strains which may exist. These can only be revealed by cutting the structure in some way and measuring the change in strain due to the cut.

With these preliminary remarks, we may now discuss some of the considerations controlling the choice of a nominal design stress. This choice will depend primarily on the type of failure to be guarded against, and on the degree of assurance required. Some possible types of failure will be discussed, along with their attendant nominal stress considerations, leaving our prime concern, brittle fracture, to the last.

5.1.1. Excessive Elastic Deflection

This can be guarded against by known methods of calculation, based on elasticity theory, so that the design stress and the proportions of the structure can be adjusted so as to confine the deflections to acceptable limits. The resulting design stresses will, of course, be within the elastic limit of the material.

5.1.2. Elastic Instability (Buckling)

This form of failure, which occurs in slender members subjected to compression, must be guarded against by applications of known methods of calculation.[1] The permissible stresses are usually considerably lower than those which would be normally acceptable.

5.1.3. Plastic Failure

This occurs when yielding takes place over a sufficiently large region to convert the structure into a virtual mechanism, so that it collapses. The modern plasticity theory of design[2, 3] caters for this by enabling the collapse load to be calculated. A 'load factor' is then applied to confine the loading to a value which will afford the desired measure of security. In more conventional design, plastic failure is guarded against simply by keeping the design stress within the elastic limit of the material. This, however, requires some caution to avoid the possibility of undue yielding spreading from any stress concentration that may have been ignored in the design.

5.1.4. Simple Rupture

This mode of failure, due to the simple overcoming of the tensile strength of the material, is usually precluded by keeping the design stress within the elastic limit of the material. It is therefore not a hazard which need be considered in normal design, except in the eventuality of accidental gross overload.

5.1.5. Fatigue

This is a form of failure in which cracking of the material occurs under the action of many repetitions of cyclic loading. The 'fatigue life' of a structure or component, i.e. the number of cycles of stress that it can sustain before failure, depends upon the range of stress and the mean stress in the cycle. Thus, a given component, submitted to a given type of cyclic loading, can sustain a large number of cycles at low intensity (stress) or a smaller number at higher intensity. There is usually a stress level below which the component can withstand a very large, or virtually infinite, number of cycles, and this is known as the 'fatigue limit' for the given conditions. For smooth, un-notched laboratory specimens, the fatigue limit at zero mean load may be one-half or less of the tensile strength of the material, but this may be markedly reduced by the presence of notches or irregularities in the surface, or by the presence of flaws, or of damage due to welding or local cold working. Fatigue cracking is probably the most common form of failure in engineering structures and must be considered in any structure submitted to variable loads. A great deal of research has been done on the subject, and the literature is voluminous. An introduction to the subject is given by Gurney.[4] The relevance of fatigue to our present subject is that a fatigue crack, being in effect a very severe form of notch, is strongly conducive to the initiation of brittle fracture in susceptible material. The choice of design working stress under fatigue conditions must depend upon a careful study of the geometry and loading conditions, in the light of available data on the fatigue lives of similar structures or components.

5.1.6. Stress Corrosion Cracking

This form of cracking, which has been mentioned earlier (see page 40) may occur when the steel is submitted to stress for long periods in a corrosive environment. It is often difficult or impractical to control it simply by reducing the nominal stress, and design against it requires special care and knowledge. Suitable protective coatings are often used to reduce the risk. Stress corrosion cracks are of course potential sources of brittle fracture in susceptible material.

5.1.7. Brittle Fracture

It has been shown in other parts of this book that brittle fractures can occur at very low nominal stresses, of the order of $\frac{1}{4}$ of the yield point of the material. The liability to brittle fracture is thus comparatively little affected by nominal stress level alone, but rather by the properties (notch ductility) of the material, and by the existence or absence of potential initiators (see Chapter 3). It is not practical, therefore, to attempt to avoid brittle fracture merely by reducing the nominal design stress alone. It is true, however, that as the nominal stress is increased, the likelihood of brittle fracture is increased and the extent of any such fracture is also increased. The higher the stress, the higher is the potential elastic energy stored in the structure, and therefore the more catastrophic is the effect of any brittle fracture. This point has to be considered, specially when high tensile steels are used.

The liability to brittle fracture is affected more by the character, rather than by the intensity, of the stress conditions. Thus, a highly triaxial stress system (i.e. one in which the three principal stresses at a point are tensile and nearly equal) is more conducive to brittle fracture than a uniaxial system of the same intensity. Also, a type of stress system that varies rapidly, such as in impact, shock, or intense vibration, causing high rates of local strain, is known to be conducive. Such conditions can sometimes be ameliorated in the design stage, and this should be done wherever possible.

In view of these circumstances, it is usual to choose the nominal design stress on the basis of other considerations, such as those mentioned earlier in this section, and to guard against brittle fracture by eliminating, as far as possible, the conducive factors (Chapter 3) and by providing for adequate notch ductility in the steel selected.

5.2. DESIGN FOR WELDING

In the context of this manual, the importance of welding lies in the fact that brittle fractures are almost always associated with stress concentrations of one kind or another and that welding is liable to produce or aggravate these.

The risk of its doing so may be incurred either at the design stage or through imperfect workmanship and inspection. Any eccentricities of loading, abrupt changes in section or discontinuities that give rise to stress concentrations are undesirable in themselves; but it does not follow that any design not completely free from such features stands to be condemned out of hand. Engineering is always conditioned by economics and good design consists in accomplishing a specified purpose at minimum cost without occasioning risks that ought to be adjudged unreasonable in the circumstances to which the structure will be exposed. What matters is that the degree of risk should be appreciated and that its acceptance or non-acceptance should be decided by informed judgement.

Brittle fractures in welded structures have almost always started at welds. This may be for any or all of three reasons, i.e. cracks or defects in the welds; insufficient notch ductility in the heat affected zones, or the effects of residual stress. Moreover, the design detail of a welded connection may be such that the welder's task is difficult and so gives rise to weld defects associated with high local stress concentrations. Such stress concentrations can arise from material defects but in practice brittle fractures are often associated with a design detail which, in the particular circumstances, has overtaxed the notch toughness of the steel.

This situation can be aggravated if secondary stresses resulting from eccentricity of load are ignored or if there are severe concentrations of stress due to changes of section, sharp re-entrant corners, or other discontinuities. Such details are themselves undesirable in that they lead to high local stresses, particularly if the start or stop of a weld, or a weld defect, coincides with a

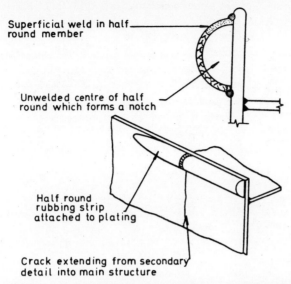

Superficial weld in half round member

Unwelded centre of half round which forms a notch

Half round rubbing strip attached to plating

Crack extending from secondary detail into main structure

Fig. 5.1. *Cracks can originate from partial penetration butt welds. Welds in minor details attached to primary structure should be treated as major welds. Recommended procedure: Joints in half round to be full strength butt welds*

point of high stress. Indeed a design detail that gives rise to high local stresses is often associated with a weld defect because the awkwardness of the detail makes the welder's task more difficult. The designer compelled by circumstances to adopt a detail which is not entirely satisfactory in this context may not, by that alone, be creating a dangerous component, but he must realise that he is adding to the debit side of the balance of factors which will in total decide whether or not the structure will be safe against failure by brittle fracture.

This chapter, with examples of details, shown in Figs. 5.1 to 5.8, therefore sets out certain principles of detail design which if followed would reduce the risk of brittle fracture. It may, however, be more economic to use a more notch ductile—and more expensive—steel and so allow greater latitude in the choice of detail.

The choice of detail is, of course, not only influenced by the possibility of brittle fracture, but also by other forms of failure referred to in the previous section. However, the principles illustrated in Figs. 5.1 to 5.8 are mainly concerned with minimising 'stress raisers' and as such are of all round benefit. This is particularly true under fatigue conditions, where higher working stresses may be adopted if due attention is given to detail design according to the principles illustrated (see BS:153). Some of the details in the illustrations are taken, with acknowledgement from a booklet published by Lloyds' Register of Shipping.[5]

There are, of course, other factors which contribute to the risk of brittle fracture, such as the accuracy of fit-up and the welding procedure, which can affect residual stress distributions; the type of electrode and welding process,

Details which can lead to cracking:-

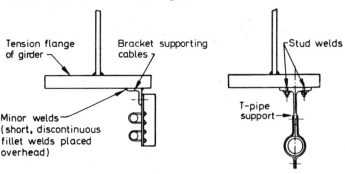

Preferred details:-

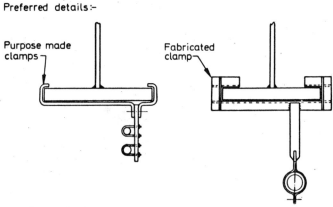

Fig. 5.2. *In the attachment of cleats or similar secondary members to primary structure, particular care must be taken to ensure that cracks are not induced by injudicious welding procedure and that the fatigue strength of the main member of which they are attached is not reduced below its design value—see BS:153. Where isolated minor welds for supports, etc., cannot be avoided there is preference for siting them on frames or transverse stiffeners in ship structures, and at about one quarter span from end supports where local bending stresses are low*

the rate at which load may be applied to the structure, and so on. Not all of these, however, are under the control of the designer but the following principles, which are matters of design, are particularly important:

1. Minimise stress concentration by avoiding abrupt changes of shape or section in stressed members, and as far as possible avoid welding minor fittings to main stressed members.
2. Make sure that the welds are placed in positions which allow adequate access for welding and inspection.
3. Avoid, as far as possible, placing welds in positions of high stress concentration.

With regard to the fixing of minor fittings, such as brackets for services, it is important to remember that these are often added on site by the

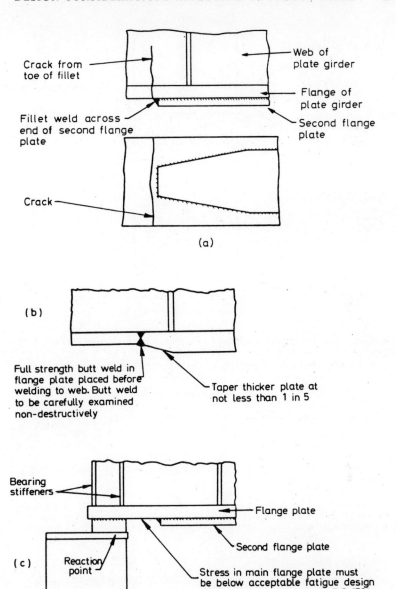

Fig. 5.3. *Care must be exercised when using fillet welds for attaching the load bearing members to main structure for reasons already stated—having regard for the notch ductility of the material and the fatigue endurance of the detail; (a) shows how some cracks have occurred at transverse fillet welds; (b) shows recommended procedure using thicker (or wider) plate where required over central section of girder and connected by transverse butt welds; (c) shows how cover plate can be run into region of compressive stress or low tensile stress before curtailment. Practices vary on the advisability of continuing the connecting fillet weld around the end of the plate. This is a design decision which has to be based on a number of factors including corrosion*

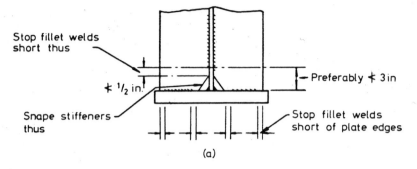

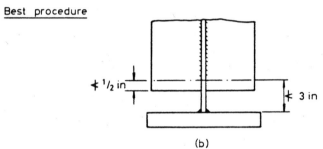

Fig. 5.4. *(a) avoid connecting stiffeners to tension flanges wherever possible. Where this is unavoidable, care should be taken to avoid overlapping welds and to ensure good welding free from defects such as root cracking and undercut; (b) illustrates best procedure*

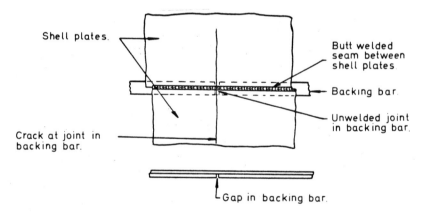

Fig. 5.5. *Discontinuities in backing bars should be avoided. Therefore use of permanent backing bars in strength welds should be avoided wherever practicable. When backing bars are unavoidable, special care must be taken with fitting up and welding. All butts in backing bars must be welded and dressed flush before fitting*

contractor installing the services, rather than by the fabricator of the structure. If welding is employed it is usually of inferior quality. The designer should try to discover beforehand what items of this sort are likely to be required and provide suitable, properly designed, attachments to be fitted in the fabricating shops. The services can then be attached to these rather than

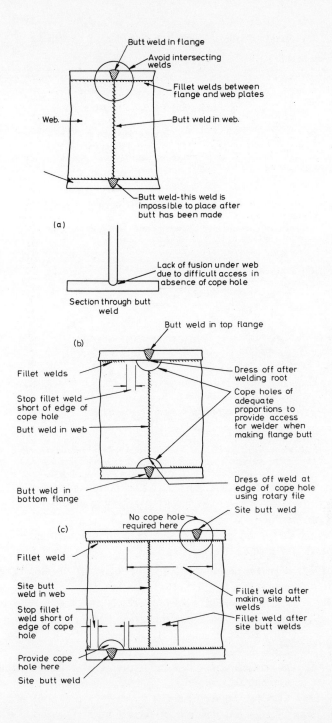

Fig. 5.6. *Cope holes should be used only where good welding would otherwise be impracticable or impossible. They should be large enough to ensure good welding. (a) shows details which can lead to cracking. (b) and (c) illustrate preferred procedure. The welding sequence is first, make butt welds in flanges, secondly, make butt welds in web and finally, complete web/flange fillet welding*

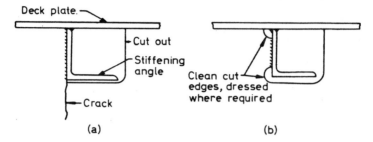

Fig. 5.7. *(a) cut-outs with sharp corners, particularly at ends of weld runs, can give rise to cracking and should be avoided. (b) all slots in tension fields should be cleanly cut with rounded corners and should be collared in the way of a concentrated load*

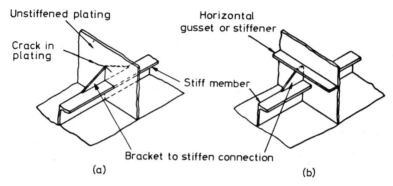

Fig. 5.8. *(a) shows a detail which can lead to cracking and should therefore be avoided. (b) shows recommended procedure to avoid cracking*

haphazardly to main members. Alternatively, clamps can be devised as shown in Fig. 5.2. The designer should specify precisely to what parts of the structure it is permissible to weld attachments.

The actual details adopted will depend on the governing specifications for the particular type of structure, such as:

BS:938:1962   General requirements for the metal-arc welding of structural steel tubes to BS:1775.

BS:1500   Fusion welded pressure vessels for use in the chemical, petroleum and allied industries. Part 1:1958 Carbon and low alloy steels.

BS:1515   Fusion welded pressure vessels for use in the chemical, petroleum and allied industries. Part 1 Carbon and ferritic alloy steels.

BS:1856:1964 General requirements for the metal arc welding of mild steel.

BS:2633:1966 Class 1 arc welding of ferritic steel pipework for carrying fluids.

BS:2642:1965 General requirements for the arc welding of steel to BS:968 and similar steels. (Note BS:968 has now been incorporated in BS:4360:1968)

BS:2971:1961 Class II metal-arc welding of steel pipelines and pipe assemblies for carrying fluids.

5.3. PRE-LOADING AND PROOF LOADING

In many types of engineering structures it is customary, as part of the construction and acceptance procedure, to apply loading under controlled conditions. Examples of this are the hydrostatic testing of pressure vessels and the test loading of bridges, cranes, etc. This loading, which is sometimes in excess of the loading anticipated in service, is applied for various purposes and with various intentions, which differ according to the type of structure, the intended service and the philosophies of individual designers. Such preloading is indeed a requirement of some specifications and codes of practice, which, however, do not always indicate the purpose or intention. In this book we are concerned with brittle fracture, and the object of the following discussion is to consider the relevance of pre-loading to the liability of a structure to brittle fracture in service. The problem has been fully reviewed by Nichols.[6]

Broadly speaking, the main objectives of pre-loading are either:

1. To prove that the structure is capable of safely sustaining the designed loading, or
2. To increase the load-carrying capacity of the structure.

The first of these, which is the most common, entails loading the completed structure to an extent and under conditions which will simulate the worst loading and conditions likely to be sustained in service, or perhaps slightly more severe to allow for contingencies. Such testing, of course, is attended by the hazard that the structure might fail under test, and consequently precautions have to be taken to avoid excessive damage or danger to personnel during the operation.

The second objective entails applying loading in excess of the normal design loading, in order to produce local or general yielding and thereby to raise the range of elastic behaviour of the structure. An example of this is the pre-loading of pipelines to a stress somewhat above the normal yield point of the material, which, for some steels, raises the effective yield point and so permits higher working stresses. A further objective of this procedure is to 'round out' irregularities in the cross-section of the pipe. This procedure should only be applied when the service loading is not likely to cause stresses in the reverse direction to that of the pre-loading at any part of the structure. This is because raising the yield point by overstressing in one direction (say tension) reduces it for stressing in the opposite direction (say compression). This effect becomes specially important in structures subjected to reversals of load in service, for which the practice is not to be recommended.

A third type of pre-loading which may be mentioned is known as 'elastic pre-stressing', consisting in applying stresses within the elastic range to strategic parts of the structure in such directions as to oppose the anticipated service stresses. The applied pre-stressing is 'built-in' to the structure so that higher service stresses than those which would be allowable by normal design can be applied without causing yielding. This practice also has to be used judiciously, and is useless, or even detrimental, if service loading may occur in the opposite direction to that intended.

Whatever the intentions of such practices, they must have certain effects on the structure and on the material of which it is composed. The relevance of these real effects to the liability to brittle fracture will now be discussed.

The effects are partly mechanical and partly metallurgical, and it is not possible to separate these, so they will be discussed together.

5.3.1. Changes in Residual Stress Patterns

Any pre-loading which causes yielding at any part of a structure will cause changes in the pre-existing pattern of residual stress. It is usually very difficult, in real structures, to predict what these changes will be, or to estimate the resultant residual stress patterns. The general relationship between residual stress and brittle fracture depends on the notch ductility of the material at the relevant temperature. If the material is in a fully notch ductile condition, residual stresses have little effect, since the superimposition of service stresses merely causes slight further local yielding, without fracture. If, however, the material is in a fully brittle condition, the residual stresses will act in the same way as any other kind of stress, so that if the resultant of the residual and service stress is tensile at the location of a notch effect, whether designed or accidental, a brittle fracture can occur. In most actual cases the material is likely to be in an intermediate condition, between notch ductile and notch brittle, and the liability to brittle fracture can only be roughly estimated. In general, therefore, the aim should be to minimise tensile residual stresses in the vicinity of notch effects.

It is, however, possible to introduce a compressive residual stress pattern at notch effects by pre-loading in tension. This must, however, be done at a sufficiently high temperature to ensure that the material has sufficient notch ductility to preclude the occurrence of a brittle fracture during the operation. Such deliberately produced compressive residual stress fields in the vicinity of notches or latent crack-like defects very probably reduce the risk of a brittle fracture originating from them. The operation should, however, be undertaken with care, to avoid the possibility of introducing adverse residual stress patterns at some locations.

5.3.2. Effects of Latent Flaws

In any real structure there must be at least a few undetected small flaws, cracks, or similar defects. The effects of preloading on these are twofold. Firstly, local yielding will usually occur around them, and this will have the effect of causing local residual stress fields, which as discussed above will usually be beneficial provided that the service loading does not reverse them. Secondly, if the flaws are in a field of tensile service stress, there will be a tendency for them to open out and for their tips to become blunted. This again will be beneficial in regard to brittle fracture, provided that the material is sufficiently notch ductile to accommodate the local yielding without extending the crack-like flaws or producing a brittle fracture. In general, therefore, the effects of preloading on latent flaws will be beneficial, provided that during the operation the material is adequately notch ductile. This can be ensured by warming the structure to a temperature at which the material is known to be notch ductile.

5.3.3. Metallurgical Damage

It is well known that many types of steel, when subjected to yielding and then 'aged', suffer a deterioration in notch ductility. The 'ageing' process is a combination of time and temperature. Thus a long period (say, several months) at room temperature, or a shorter period at a higher temperature, say, one hour at 250° C, produce the full 'strain ageing' effect, provided that the material has been previously strained about 2% or 5%. Such treatment may raise the transition temperature of the steel by 30° or 40° C. Pre-loading, or indeed any loading of a structure is likely to cause local yielding at any sharp notch effect, crack or crack-like flaw even when the nominal stresses are quite low, and within the nominal elastic range. It follows, then, that strain ageing, with consequent deterioration in notch ductility can occur locally at such positions, and this must be offset against the beneficial effects discussed in Section 5.3.2 above. This deterioration can be, to a large extent, removed by judicious 'stress relief' heat treatment, if this is practicable.

The effects of straining and ageing are not, however, entirely detrimental. They may, for example, raise the yield point of the material, and this can to some extent resist the initiation of a crack.

Summarising the foregoing, it can be seen that in the present state of knowledge it must remain a matter of opinion whether overstressing is beneficial from the viewpoint of liability to brittle fracture. On balance, it is generally regarded as beneficial, subject to some important provisos as follow:

1. The overstressing should be applied in the same direction as the antici-pated service loading. If the structure is to be subjected to reversals of loading or local reversals of stress, the overstressing should not greatly exceed the designed service load, to avoid extensive yielding.
2. The overstressing should be applied at a sufficiently high temperature to ensure that the material is in an adequately notch ductile condition.
3. Suitable precautions should be taken to minimise possible danger to personnel or consequential damage occurring during the process of overstressing.
4. Before applying an overstress, it is desirable to inspect the structure thoroughly to ensure that there are no defects likely to initiate a fracture,

and in particular to ensure that there are no long crack-like defects or stress concentrations, such as could lead to strains exceeding about 2% in their vicinity. This is particularly important in structures which may be heated in service, since this can cause local strain ageing in the strained areas.

5. Overstressing, or warm proof testing, should not be regarded as a cheap substitute for thermal stress relief heat treatment, but as an expedient which might be adopted if thermal stress relief treatment is impracticable.

6. A successful proof test should not, in itself, be regarded as a guarantee that brittle fracture will not occur in service. It has been shown in other parts of this book that brittle fracture can, in certain circumstances, occur at low nominal stresses, and therefore there can be no guarantee that it will not occur if the service conditions, such as temperature, rate of loading, etc., are more severe than those prevailing during the proof loading. Such changes in conditions must be guarded against by other means, such as ensuring adequate notch ductility, absence of defects, thermal stress relief, and so on, as indicated in other Chapters.

References

1. TIMOSHENKO, S., *Theory of Elastic Stability*, McGraw-Hill Book Co. (1936)
2. BAKER, J. F., 'The design of steel frames', *The Structural Engineer* (*Journal of the Instn. of Structural Engineers*), 27, No 10, 397–431 (October, 1949)
3. HILL, R., *Mathematical Theory of Plasticity*, Oxford University Press (1950)
4. GURNEY, T. R., *Fatigue of Welded Structures*, Cambridge University Press (1968)
5. Lloyds Register of Shipping, *Detail Design in Ships* (October, 1967)
6. NICHOLS, R. W., *The Use of Overstressing Techniques to reduce the risk of subsequent brittle fracture*, IIW Commission X 1967 X-409-67E

CHAPTER 6

REVIEW OF CURRENT METHODS FOR STEEL SELECTION

This Chapter will briefly recount the endeavours that have been made during the past thirty years, and are still proceeding, to evolve rational principles for specifying and controlling the manufacture and use of steels so as to minimise the risk of brittle fracture.

It has already been stated that it is not possible to achieve effective correlation between test results and the behaviour of steel in service nor to correlate the results of one type of test with those of another. The many attempts that have been made have served more to reveal the complexities of the problem than to clarify it.

However, several attempts have been made to evolve coherent philosophies for the selection of materials, and some of these will be described.

6.1. THE TRENDS OF BRITISH PRACTICE

6.1.1. General

Current British practice in the choice of steels is essentially pragmatic, having been in evolution from a time before there was any scientific foundation on which to base it. The account of it given here is therefore a description of what prevails rather than an advocacy of what may be desirable.

It is generally agreed that a higher degree of assurance against brittle fracture is required in some structures than in others. Whereas in some isolated minor piece of equipment the consequences of a brittle crack might only be local, a crack propagating through a whole ship or bridge, or for thousands of feet along a pipeline, would be very serious. At the same time it must be remembered that failure of even a minor component might prejudice the operation of a large plant or structure.

In all cases it is necessary to choose steel having a level of notch ductility which is adequate but, in the interests of economy, not excessive. Although criteria giving adequate safety can be defined, it is not yet possible to determine these accurately in terms of optimum economy.

It is recognised that for a limited range of special applications it is desirable to use steels capable of arresting a freely propagating brittle crack at the lowest temperature likely to be encountered in service. For these special applications the suitability of the steel is usually judged on the basis of experience of its use in similar structures or by the Robertson isothermal crack arrest temperature (see Chapter 4). For the purpose of quality control and batch acceptance tests, the V-notch Charpy impact test (see Chapter 4) is generally used on the basis of empirical correlation with the Robertson crack arrest test, or with service experience.

For structural applications involving static loading only, e.g. pressure vessels and storage tanks, it is generally accepted in Britain that the integrity of such a structure is adequately safeguarded if the steel offers sufficient resistance to crack initiation, to which the Robertson test is not applicable. As the circumstances capable of initiating cracks are recognised as being enormously varied, the selection of steels for these purposes has long been based on judgement and experience, although the subject has been extensively studied in the last few years by means of the Wells/BWRA Wide Plate test and various fracture mechanics tests (see Chapter 4).

For most ordinary structures, it has been considered in the past that an adequate safeguard against brittle fracture would be provided if at the lowest anticipated service temperature, the steel absorbs 20 ft lb (2·8 kg m), in the Charpy V-notch test with specimens cut in the direction of rolling, or 15 ft lb (2·1 kg m) in the transverse direction. It has now become clear as a result of Wide Plate and Crack Opening Displacement (COD) Tests[1] that this simple criterion is open to question for various reasons, and particularly because of the important effect of thickness which is not revealed by the Charpy test. It is necessary to provide more notch ductility, as determined by the Charpy V test, for thick steels than for thin. This can be achieved by increasing the energy required to be absorbed at a given temperature or, alternatively, by requiring that a standard energy absorption value should be achieved at a lower temperature. These two approaches are equivalent in their effects and both are employed in British design procedures.

On the other hand it is accepted that in certain other circumstances the usual requirement as to notch ductility can safely be relaxed. For example it is frequently assumed that at normal ambient temperatures no brittle fracture hazard exists in statically loaded mild steel weldments of reasonable thickness if the weldment is effectively 'stress relieved' by post heat treatment.

Though it is commonly assumed that the impact value needs to be greater where the nominal stress level is unusually high, as for example when a high tensile steel is to be used, there is at present no uniformity of practice in regard to the amount of this additional safety margin. Lloyd's Rules for ships require that the Charpy energy is to be increased in proportion to the square root of yield point plus tensile strength.[2]

The Charpy V-notch test has been widely used for the selection of carbon and carbon-manganese steels, alloy and quenched and tempered steels but the validity of its use beyond the range of simple carbon and carbon-manganese steels has not been well-established.

6.1.2. Significance of the Wide Plate Test

Whilst British practice in recent years in selecting materials to avoid brittle fracture has been based largely on empirical methods, there has been a recent trend towards the adoption of a philosophy based upon direct comparison of results of notched and welded Wells/BWRA Wide Plate tests with service performance. This philosophy is aimed at the prevention of fracture initiation, for which purpose the test is well adapted. Since, however, these tests are usually carried out under static loading conditions the results should not be applied to structures subjected to impact loading.

A special feature of the notched and welded Wide Plate test is that it reproduces the observed service phenomena of low stress brittle fracture in the laboratory. For a particular steel and fabrication technique, tests at different temperatures show transitional behaviour and below a certain temperature fractures can occur at low applied stresses. Above this transition temperature fracture does not occur until a certain amount of general plastic strain has been sustained by the specimen. The test is primarily concerned with conditions for initiation of fracture from a defect associated with welding, and can be regarded as sufficiently large to simulate the service behaviour of a structure. The test is carried out on material at full plate thickness and so automatically takes into account both geometric and metallurigcal effects of thickness as well as the effects of welding.

In many structures there are regions of stress concentration which in some cases are sufficient to cause local yielding and plastic strains over a significant region. An example of this behaviour is given by the situation at nozzles in pressure vessels, in which it is possible to calculate the maximum amount of plastic strain which will occur under the most severe loading conditions. For mild steel pressure vessels, designed for a working stress equal to two-thirds of the yield stress and with a design stress concentration factor of 2·5 at the nozzles, the maximum shear strain likely to occur during the initial proof test to 1·3 × design pressure will not usually exceed 0·5% which is of the order of 4 times the yield point elastic strain.

By assessing the results of notched and welded Wide Plate tests in terms of the plastic strain required to initiate fracture in the test, related to the above expected strain, a criterion can be derived which can be applied to the selection of materials. Materials selected to meet this criterion can then be considered suitable for the type of service for which this comparison is valid.

It should be borne in mind, when making use of wide plate test data that the type, size and location of the notch are arbitrary, and the results may be influenced by these variables. The results are also influenced by the local metallurgical conditions at the root of the notch, and by the criterion adopted for 'failure' in the test. In practice, the criterion arbitrarily adopted is 0·5% strain over a gauge length of 20 in (510 mm), and this has been found to correlate reasonably well with the strains to be expected at actual design discontinuities as discussed above.

6.1.3. Problems of Arresting a Running Crack

When it is necessary to design against the possibility of propagation of a brittle fracture as, for example, when it may have to be envisaged that dynamic loading, in the presence of minor weld defects may lead to a fast running crack entering the parent plate, judgement is usually based upon crack arrest type test results. It is assumed that if the steel is used above its crack arrest temperature in such a test the structure will not develop a catastrophic brittle fracture.

For the purpose of production control, instead of making actual crack arrest tests, it is usual to adopt a Charpy V-notch energy level that has been found to correlate with the crack arrest temperature for the particular steel and plate thickness.

This approach had been criticised as providing an over safe and therefore extravagant criterion for general structural applications. Furthermore the theory of fracture mechanics indicates that a tough steel could only be expected to arrest a running crack if the crack length is not greater than the critical value for initiation in the nominal stress field considered. This could only happen in a constant stress field where the crack starts in an area of local embrittlement. In general, however, crack arrest can only be expected if the fracture propagates into a stress field of lower intensity than that at the point of initiation, or if there is a mechanical barrier in the structure, e.g. a riveted seam. Bevitt et al.[3] conducted bursting tests on pressure vessels having axial artificial faults in the cylindrical shells. They showed that, irrespective of the service temperature, a running crack could not be arrested if the stress in the shell was maintained by the use of gas, instead of a liquid as the testing fluid.

It has been established that over the range of temperature in which the fracture of steel changes from cleavage to shear type, the velocity of crack propagation decreases somewhat with increasing temperature and fragmentation becomes less likely to occur. It appears that the reduction in the velocity of the crack with increasing toughness (due to increase in temperature) is sufficient to permit some relaxation of load, and so bring about arrest at the level of toughness corresponding to that found in the isothermal Robertson (see page 51) or the Double Tension Test (see page 57).

6.2. TRENDS IN OTHER COUNTRIES

Various other methods have been proposed from time to time to give guidance in the choice of materials, and these have been under continuous review by Commissions XI and XV of the International Institute of Welding, the Navy Department Advisory Committee on Structural Steels and elsewhere. Some of these techniques are summarised here.

The system developed under the leadership of Pellini and Puzak in the Metallurgy Division of the United States Naval Research Laboratory is described in a report entitled 'Fracture analysis diagram procedures for the fracture-safe engineering design of steel structures,'[4] and in another report referring especially to pressure vessels.[5] These appeared in 1963 and have been followed by a third report[6] which reviews the concept and status of each procedure for what is described as the fracture-safe design of complex welded structures at all stress levels.

The authors of these reports consider that earlier attempts to elucidate the brittle fracture problem by using the transition temperature approach have been hampered by inability to allow for the effects of residual stress and variations in the size of flaws. To remedy this deficiency they provide what they call a 'package approach' offering a combination of:

1. Practical testing procedures using simple equipment;
2. A simple method of analysis with allowances for the main operative factors, including flaw size;
3. Flexibility of application;
4. A background of successful applications in respect of service failures and tests simulating service conditions.

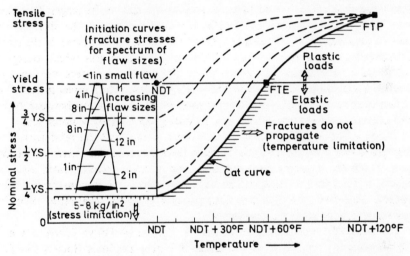

Fig. 6.1. *Generalised fracture analysis diagram, as referenced by the NDT temperature*

The generalised fracture analysis diagram (FAD) proposed by Pellini and collaborators[4] is reproduced in Fig. 6.1, from which it will be seen that the diagram consists of a notional plot of nominal stress versus temperature. The CAT (Crack Arrest Temperature) curve, shown as a shaded full line, represents the stresses and corresponding temperatures at which a running brittle fracture would be arrested. It is postulated that to the right and below this curve fractures do not propagate, whereas to the left and above the curve, fractures may or may not propagate, depending upon the size of flaws or initiating cracks present. As suggested in the diagram, if flaws are small or non-existent, the conditions for initiation and propagation are determined by the uppermost of the dotted curves. Increasing the flaw size has the effect of lowering the critical stress, as suggested by the family of dotted curves.

It is assumed that such a diagram can be plotted from experimental data for any given steel, and would determine the temperature-stress conditions at which a flaw of given size could develop into a running brittle fracture. In practice, however, the complete determination of such a diagram by experimental methods would be extremely costly, but the authors have derived, from long experience and accumulated data, empirical methods by which the diagram can be constructed approximately, as follows:

The NDT (Nil Ductility Temperature) is determined by means of the Drop Weight Test (see Chapter 4). This, combined with the yield and tensile strength of the steel gives the significant points on the diagram by adding the temperature increments indicated on the baseline (Fig. 6.1). The lower (horizontal) limb of the CAT curve can be determined from Robertson or Double Tension Tests (see Chapter 4), but for most structural steels it can be assumed to be at about 2–4 ton/in^2 (30–60 N/mm^2).

The diagram provides a useful frame of reference to assist engineering judgement in the choice of steels. For example in a given structure, if the stress and temperature conditions, as well as the size of the largest flaw that may be expected, are known or can be confidently assumed, the diagram can help to indicate the NDT temperature which should be required of the steel. Conversely the diagram can be used to analyse fractures which occur in service, and to assist in the evaluation of experience. Engineers who wish to use the diagram are recommended to study the description given in Refs 4–6 in this chapter which also give information on the correlation between NDT and criteria derived from other tests, including the Charpy V-notch test.

The practical significance of the reference points and the relationship of the tests to the fracture analysis diagram have not received universal acceptance. Since the diagram does not take into account loading rates and the effects of thickness its application to actual structures is considered to be limited. However, the diagram does provide a useful qualitative tool for assessing weldments in general terms.

The method developed by Professor H. Kihara of Tokyo University and his co-workers[7] on behalf of the Japan Welding Engineer Society (JWES) can be summarily described as a system for grading batches of steel plates in terms of their relevant properties including the service conditions for which they are regarded as suitable, as inferred from certain tests and expressed by code designations.

The system links fracture mechanics theory with the results of the Double Tension Crack Arrest test, leading to a system of designations for steel plate.

As an example, a particular batch of steel plates might be designated

LT 32–II–90 G

where the successive code symbols have the following significance:

LT = this steel is suitable for low temperature service;

32 = its nominal guaranteed yield strength is 32 kg/mm^2;

II = the plate thickness is within range II among the six ranges defined (e.g., range I = 5–13 mm, range IV = 40–50 mm but the actual thickness or tolerance within the limits of the range is not stated.)

90 = the lowest permissible service temperature is $-90°$ C (seven temperature ranges being distinguished, down to respectively $0°$ C, $-30°$ C, $-50°$ C, $-70°$ C, $-90°$ C, $-110°$ C, $-170°$ C);

G = a normal hazard of brittle fracture is assumed, whereas the alternative letter *A* would relate to a material which is able to arrest a brittle crack if one has been initiated.

Steel plate to each grade must meet specified yield stress, tensile strength, percentage elongation, cold bend and Charpy V-notch requirements at defined temperatures. The minimum temperature of service to which plate of a particular grade may be used is based on a correlation between the fracture toughness of steel required to arrest a running crack, and the temperature. It is claimed that the transition temperature obtained from a pressed notch Charpy test corresponds to a particular level of fracture toughness. This test could therefore be used for reference purposes, but for practical reasons preference has been given to the standard Charpy V-notch test using statistical correlations with the pressed notch Charpy test.

Before a grade of steel is included in the specification, tests for weldability, fracture toughness and other characteristics must be made on typical material and the results submitted for consideration by JWES. In general the fracture toughness-temperature relationship is determined by Double Tension tests on plate of a standard thickness (usually 30 mm). The transition temperatures are also determined by the pressed notch Charpy test and the Charpy V-notch test. Further Double Tension tests may be made on plate of reduced thicknesses to establish the relationship between fracture toughness and thickness.

The criterion for acceptance on a production basis is that the Charpy V-notch test shall display more than a certain level of energy at a single reference temperature. This minimum energy level is one half of the energy corresponding to 100% fibrous fracture.

In deriving this reference temperature it is considered that the minimum allowable service temperature depends on the design stress, the tolerable crack length and the plate thickness. Co-operation between those responsible for steel quality and for application standards has resulted in the specification of minimum service temperatures on this basis with adjustments to suit different types of structure and service conditions.

This system is attractive in both approach and practical interpretation. Its reliability depends, however, on the reproducibility of the results of the tests; on the degree of correlation between the results of double tension tests and the Charpy V-notch test; and on the validity of adjustments for different applications. JWES has adopted a cautious approach with standards which are based on the systems. In the United Kingdom there is little first hand experience of the Double Tension test, used as above, or in conjunction with pressed notch or V-notch Charpy tests. Developments are however being followed with keen interest.

It is interesting to note that recently there has been a change in the proposed bases of the main Groups G and A.[8-10] Originally both of these Groups were related to conditions for the arrest of a fracture. G signified the probability of arrest within a crack length of 10 mm, while A signified arrest within 100 mm. In the latest proposals the basis of A remains unchanged, but G is related to the probable initiation of a fracture from a crack not less than 100 mm long. The fracture initiation conditions for steel plate of particular grades are determined by deep notch tension tests. The test specimen is 400 mm wide × 500 mm long and of full plate thickness. Symmetrical deep and sharp notches (80 mm deep) are cut at the mid-length and normal to the longer sides. Tension tests at different temperatures on a number of specimens are made to evaluate the fracture toughness versus temperature characteristics of the steel.

In Germany a system worked out by the Deutsche Ausschuss für Stahlbau (DAST)[11] is based on the use of cumulative 'points' for each kind of structure and for each kind of steel and assumes that the total points for structure and for steel can be matched against each other. The points, or indices, are assessed separately for each criterion of fracture and are then summed to determine the 'danger value' for the structure. This total is compared with the total of the similar indices attributed to 'quality values' for the various steels. The factors considered in deriving the indices are as follows:

1. The applied and residual stresses, triaxiality and dead load stresses.
2. Situation of welds, complexity and accessibility.
3. Thickness.
4. Temperature.
5. Work hardening or constraint or both.
6. Importance of the integrity of the structure.

Although the system has been adopted to some extent in Germany, it has aroused some misgivings elsewhere mainly because it rests on the assumption that each steel and each structure has a characteristic transition temperature and that these can be matched. The evidence for this is by no means clear. It can further be argued that the controlling factors such as those listed above are not simply additive or independent of one another. Nevertheless the system is simple and useful in experienced hands, provided that the points assigned to each factor are suitably chosen. Its application must clearly be tempered by judgement, particularly in extreme circumstances such as large structures, thick sections and extremes of temperature.

In the Soviet Union, rules have been developed which involve type testing for each grade of steel. The three sets of tests in use, as described by Kanfor,[12] appear to be for steels intended for use in welded seagoing merchant ships which have to navigate in ice and may be summarised as follows:

1. Tests of small V-notched specimens in static bending to determine the 'critical brittleness' temperature as defined in the rules of the USSR Shipping Register. These are performed on specimens very similar in form and dimensions to the Charpy V-notch test piece shown by Fig. 4.2.

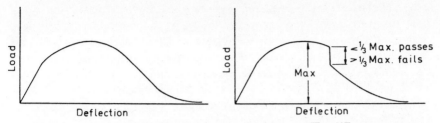

Figs. 6.2 and 6.3. *Load/deflection curve of small notched specimens in slow bending*

The test is carried out in a press and a load/deflection curve is determined. If this curve is of the type shown at *A* in Fig. 6.2 it indicates ductile propagation of the crack which is assumed to initiate from the notch at or near the maximum load, and is regarded as satisfactory. If, however, the curve is of type *B* in Fig. 6.3 with a sharp discontinuity and a sudden drop in load due to brittle propagation of a crack, the result is assessed by the extent of this drop which should be less than one third of the maximum load. Tests are made over a range of temperatures to ascertain the lowest temperature at which a satisfactory result is obtained. This must not be higher than 0° C if the steel is to pass the test.

2. Tests of large notched specimens to determine the critical brittleness temperature from the type of fracture. The test piece is of full plate thickness and has a V-notch. No other details are given, but the test may be assumed to be substantially similar to that of Van der Veen (page 53) using different criteria. For plate of ordinary thickness the criterion is that the temperature corresponding to 70% fibrous fracture, should not be higher than 30° C. For 'high gauge' plate (which appears to mean a thickness of approximately ¾ in) it is that the temperature for a 30% fibrous fracture should not be higher than 0° C.

3. Mesnager type (see Fig. 4.2) impact bending tests to determine the ductility of the steel according to impact energy temperature curves. These are primarily energy absorption tests, but there are suggestions[12] that they could also be used as fracture appearance tests.

When on the basis of its overall performance in these three series of tests, a steel is judged to show suitable resistance to brittle fracture for the desired application, its control and inspection from that point of view are carried out by means of the impact test alone with an appropriate energy requirement at a specified temperature, usually −40° C.

Difficulty was experienced in obtaining detailed information on this procedure and its inclusion in this book is intended merely as a general indication of the Russian approach to the problem.

6.3. FRACTURE MECHANICS

As early as 1921, A. A. Griffith[13] had laid the foundations of the theoretical study, later called fracture mechanics, which seeks to account for the propagation of cracks in terms of energy balances (see Chapter 2). It was not, how-ever, till nearly thirty years later that the work of Irwin[14-16] and, indepen-dently, of Orowan[17, 18] followed by that of others such as Wells,[19] and Boyd[20] made it possible to achieve some progress in transferring ideas from the ideally brittle elastic material (glass) assumed by Griffith to materials which are capable of plastic deformation before fracture. (A bibliography citing 33 references to the subject, is appended to a paper by van den Boogaart and Turner.[21]

Fracture mechanics seeks to explain on the macroscale how the overall strength of a component is related to its shape and size and to the mechanical properties of the material. It has been applied with some success to the notched static strength of materials, particularly those in sheet form, that have a high ratio of strength to density, such as ultra high strength alloy steels, and very strong aluminium or titanium alloys or the glassy plastics. More recently it has been applied to problems of environmental cracking and fatigue as well as tentatively to less strong materials. Though efforts are being made to over-come the current limitations of the theory it is still not clear how far the present approach can be extended in these directions.

The assumption is made that in any real structure very sharp cracks or other defects either exist already or will develop in service. Therefore the analysis of stresses around cracks and the testing of sharply notched pieces is the basis of this branch of fracture mechanics. Fracture mechanics does not set out to explain how a crack is initially formed but only the circum-stances in which it will spread in a given material and condition. For the purpose of linear fracture mechanics the analysis of stress around a crack is based on elastic theory with allowances made, somewhat empirically, for local plasticity. This simplification is an advantage of the present theory as it allows several simple but important answers to be derived. It has been suggested that any quantitative application should be limited to cases where fracture occurs without significant plastic deformation.

When a plate with a central or edge notch is tested in tension or by bending, the initial crack may extend slowly, and in materials for which this analysis is suitable the test terminates in rapid propagation of the crack with conse-quent complete fracture of the test piece in most circumstances. By measuring or inferring the stress level and crack length at the onset of this rapid propaga-tion it is possible to calculate the corresponding value of K, which under certain conditions (described later) is a characteristic of the material desig-nated as the 'fracture toughness'.

There is no doubt that for the high strength materials this approach correctly predicts major trends of fracture load in relation to the size of the object or the depth of the crack, but it is necessary to distinguish between results for thin sheets in which no appreciable *stress* can develop in the through thickness direction (even with local contraction at the root of the notch due to plastic flow) and thick plate in which the *strain* developed through the plate thickness at the notch root is negligible. In the former condition, referred to as 'plane stress' the K_c value obtained is dependent upon thickness and to a certain extent on temperature and strain rate, being typified by a shear fracture. In the latter condition, referred to as 'plane strain', which corresponds to a flat fracture, the fracture toughness is denoted by K_{Ic} and is independent of thickness but dependent on temperature and strain rate.

The application of linear fracture mechanics to a real design situation enables a relationship to be found between K_{Ic} of the material, permissible crack or flaw size and overall stress level. Thus, fixing a required stress level determines a maximum permissible safe crack size, or alternatively specifying the allowable maximum crack size determines the permissible operating stress.

As already mentioned, the application of linear fracture mechanics is usually restricted to materials for which fracture initiation is not preceded by significant yielding. For lower strength structural steels the linear fracture mechanics approach is often invalidated because the plastic deformation which develops at the crack tip exceeds the amount which can be satisfactorily approximated by the simple theory. Work on the assessment of the notch ductility of lower strength steels is progressing, particularly by means of the concept of Crack Opening Displacement (COD)[1, 22, 28] which is based upon fracture mechanics adapted to take account of general yielding. Crack opening displacements only become measurable when significant local plasticity occurs at the tip of a crack and these are precisely the circumstances which invalidate linear elastic analysis.

For further details of the fracture mechanics approach to low stress fracture the reader is referred to the references cited.

6.4. ANALYSIS OF SERVICE FRACTURES

It will be clear from what has been said in preceding chapters, and in the earlier part of this one, that the notch ductility of the steel is an important factor influencing the incidence of brittle fracture in service. It follows therefore that studies of the notch ductilities of the steels involved in actual service fractures should provide useful guidance for the selection of steel in the design stages.

Many such studies have been made with this objective, and some of these will now be described briefly.

One of the earliest was made at the National Bureau of Standards, Washington, USA. A large number of samples of steel plate were collected from actual service failures in welded ships, and on each of these samples a sufficient number of Charpy V-notch tests were made over a range of temperatures to produce transition curves, which were later analysed statistically.

In the statistical analysis, the criterion adopted was the temperature at which the Charpy V-notch energy was 15 ft lb (2.1 kg.m). This criterion became known as the '15 ft lb (2·1 kg.m) transition temperature', although no actual transition in properties occurred at this point, which was adopted merely because it seemed a suitably representative one in relation to the types of steels involved in the casualties investigated.

The samples were divided into three groups, designated as follows:

1. *Source Plates.* Those containing or immediately adjacent to the origins of fracture.
2. *Through Plates.* Those through which the fracture passed.
3. *End Plates.* Those in which the fracture stopped.

Distribution curves were produced for each of these groups, showing the percentage of the plates having their '15 ft lb (2·1 kg.m) transitions' in each 10° F temperature interval, and these distribution curves were compared.

The complete data is given in a series of reports, summarised by Williams.[23]

For our present purpose it is sufficient to give the figures, which emerge from the study, and are shown in Table 6.1.

Table 6.1

No of Samples	Plate Group	15 ft/lb temperature	
		Mean	Standard Deviation
28	Source Plates	96° F (36° C)	25° F (14° C)
45	Through Plates	65° F (18° C)	17° F (9·5° C)
32	End Plates	51° F (11° C)	21° F (11·5° C)
105	All samples	69° F (21° C)	19° F (10·5° C)

These figures, which are derived by scaling from the diagram given by Williams[23] are approximate, but clearly show a tendency towards lower transition temperatures for the three groups in the order 'Source'–'Through'–'End', indicating that, to reduce the probability of fractures initiating, the 15 ft lb (2·1 kg.m) temperature should be as low as possible.

This early study has been criticised on three grounds, namely:

1. that the 15 ft lb (2·1 kg.m) temperature, although it may be representative of the particular steels investigated which had low 'shelf energies', is not adequately representative for steels having transition curves showing generally higher shelf energies, as is more usual in modern structural steels.
2. That the study was confined to steels involved in fractures, and gave no indication of how their properties compared with the general populations of steels, including those which did not fracture.
3. That the study does not indicate how low the 15 ft lb (2·1 kg.m) transition should be to reduce the risk to an acceptable level.[24]

The study was nevertheless useful in indicating a relationship between temperature, incidence of fracture and steel properties.

Another important analysis of materials involved in brittle fractures in non-marine structures was made at the US Naval Research Laboratory.[25] This study was based on the 'Fracture Analysis Diagram' (see Fig. 6.1). Samples of the steels involved in each of the failures investigated were submitted to Pellini drop weight tests (see page 55), and also to Charpy V-notch tests. The information obtained from these tests together with other information, was used to construct Fracture Analysis Diagrams appropriate to each of the cases.

The results of the study, which are fully set out by Puzak *et al*[25] served to emphasise the importance of material properties in relation to temperature. They showed the usefulness of the Fracture Analysis Diagram in studies of service fracture, and of the concept of 'Nil Ductility Temperature' for assessing the notch ductility of steels. The method is, however, like all other methods so far available, subject to a considerable element of judgement in its interpretation.

In the United Kingdom, Lloyd's Register of Shipping collected a large amount of data on service fractures in ships, which data was published in a paper to the Royal Institution of Naval Architects in 1958.[26] Samples of plate involved in the fractures were submitted to a wide variety of tests, but the analysis was based mainly on the Charpy V-notch tests.

The results are summarised in Fig. 4.5. In this diagram, the test curves (Charpy V-notch energy, Charpy V-notch crystallinity, and Tipper notched tensile crystallinity versus temperature) are plotted for the steels involved in

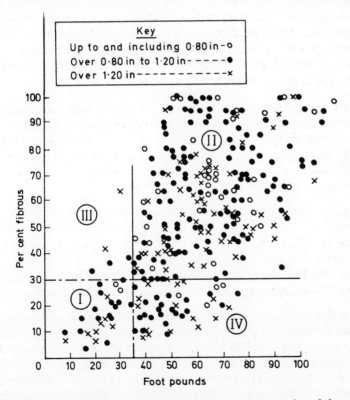

Fig. 6.4. *Plot of results of Charpy V-notch tests at 0°C on a large number of plates, taken at random from the (then) current production, varying in thickness from ¾ to 1⅛ in, of many steelworks all over the world (By courtesy of Royal Institution of Naval Architects)*

the fractures, and a symbol is placed on each curve at the temperature at which the fracture occurred. These symbols distinguish three groups of plates as follows:

1. *Success Plates* (black dots) are those which fracture in a ductile manner, or in which brittle fractures, originating outside the plate, were arrested.
2. *Failure Plates* (open circles) are those which were completely traversed by a brittle fracture.
3. *Borderline Plates* (crosses) are those which could not be classified in either of the above groups.

The following points emerge from a study of the diagram:
1. The plates involved in the fractures cover a very wide range of notch ductilities, whether measured by Charpy energy, Charpy crystallinity, or Tipper crystallinity.
2. On the basis of Charpy V-notch energy (Fig. 4.5(a)) it is virtually impossible to find a single energy/temperature point which would satisfactorily segregate the 'Failure' from the 'Success' plates over the full range of steels studied.
3. The discrimination between 'Failure' and 'Success' is somewhat better on the basis of Charpy crystallinity (Fig. 4.5(b)). It is seen that the great majority of the 'Failure' plates have crystallinities in excess of 70%.
4. There is a clear discrimination between 'Failure' and 'Success' on the basis of percentage crystallinity in the Tipper notched tensile test (Fig. 4.5(c)) but even this is subject to some uncertainty.

In order to see whether a combination of Charpy energy and crystallinity would provide adequate discrimination without recourse to the Tipper Test, Fig. 4.5(d) was plotted. This is a plot of Charpy percent fibrous (i.e. 100 minus the percentage crystallinity) against Charpy energy, both at the temperature of the casualty. It is seen that the resulting diagram could be divided with four zones, as indicated, i.e.

1. *Zone I*—Low energy, low fibrous, containing most of the 'Failure' plates.
2. *Zone II*—High energy, high fibrous, containing mainly 'Success' and 'Borderline' plates.
3. *Zone III*—Low energy—high fibrous—containing few points.
4. *Zone IV*—High energy—low fibrous—containing few points.

Taking this in conjunction with a similar diagram (Fig. 6.4) constructed from data representing the general population of available ship steels, the authors of the study concluded that it would be prudent and feasible to set a lower limit to the acceptable Charpy V-notch energy at 0° C, which is a significant temperature in relation to ships. This would exclude steels of the types (defined by Charpy energy) which were involved in the majority of the failures.

It should be noted that this study was oriented towards the ship problem,

1 Charpy 15 ft.lb transition
2   "   transition at 50% crystallinity
3   "   "   "   75%   "
4 Tipper   "   "   50%   "
5 Van der Veen   "   32 mm fibrous
6 Robertson arrest   "   10 ton/in^2
7 2 ft wide notch tensile test
8 6 ft   "   "   "   "   Robertson
9 Pellini dropweight nil ductility transit[n]
10 3 ft wide plate test

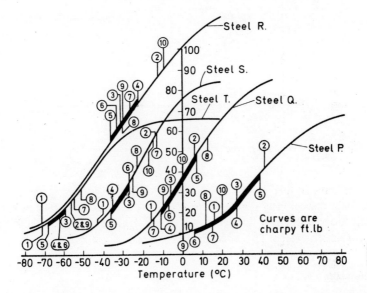

Fig. 6.5. *Diagrammatic comparison of transition temperature according to various criteria.*
N.B. Curves thickened over range of criteria 3, 4, 5 and 6 (By courtesy of H.M.S.O.)

and the results are not necessarily capable of extrapolation to structures operating at sub-zero temperatures.

It may be noted, however, from inspection of Fig. 4.5(a) that the majority of the 'Failures' occurred below the points of inflexion of the Charpy energy curves. This observation seems to have some significance when considered in relation to other studies. For example, in Fig. 4.12 it is seen that the Nil Ductility Temperatures in the Pellini Explosion Bulge Test occur in the vicinity of the points of inflexion. Again, on Fig. 6.5[27] it can be seen that the 'transition temperature', defined by various criteria in a wide variety of tests, tends to occur at or below the points of inflexion of the Charpy curves. The JWES method for assessing steels (see page 82) relies on this observation in that it regards the mid-point of the Charpy curve as having special significance for the assessment.

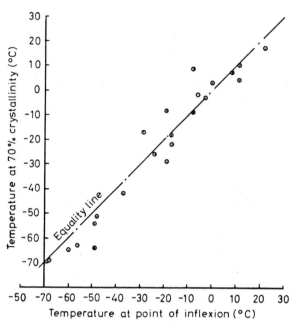

Fig. 6.6. *Correlation between 70% crystallinity and point of inflexion in the Charpy
V-notch test*

The temperature at the point of inflexion also correlates fairly well with
the 70% crystallinity temperature, which as mentioned earlier in connection
with Lloyd's Register data (Fig. 4.5(b)), is significant in relation to incidence
of service fractures. This correlation is shown in Fig. 6.6.

References

1. WELLS, A. A., 'Houdremont Lecture 1964', *British Welding Journal*, **12**, No 1,
   2–13 (January, 1965)
2. Lloyd's Register of Shipping Rules and Regulations, Section P.3 (1969)
3. BEVITT, E., COWAN, A., and STOTT, A. L., *Journal British Nuclear Energy Society*,
   3, 16 (1964)
4. PELLINI, W. S., and PUZAK, P. P., 'Fracture Analysis Diagram Procedures for the
   Fracture-safe Engineering Design of Steel Structures', *US Naval Research
   Laboratory, Washington*, Report No 5920 (March, 1963)
5. PELLINI, W. S., and PUZAK, P. P., 'Practical Considerations in Applying Laboratory
   Fracture Test Criteria to the Fracture-safe Design of Pressure Vessels', *US Naval
   Research Laboratory, Washington*, Report No 6030 (November, 1963)
6. PELLINI, W. S., *et al.*, *US Naval Research Laboratory, Washington*, Report No
   6300 (June, 1965)
7. KIHARA, H., and KANAZAWA, T., 'Evaluation Criterion of Structural Steels for
   Low Temperature Application', *International Institute of Welding*, Document
   IX-414-64 (1964)
8. KIHARA, H., and IKEDA, K., 'A proposal on Evaluation of Brittle Crack Initiation
   and Arresting Temperatures and their Application to Design of Welded
   Structures', *Ship Research Institute, Tokyo*, Paper No 14 (April, 1966)

9. IKEDA, K., and KIHARA, H., 'A Proposal on Criteria for Prevention of Welded Structure from Brittle Fracture', *Ship Research Institute, Tokyo*, Paper No 24 (December, 1967)
10. IKEDA, K., AKITA, Y., and KIHARA, H., 'The Deep Notch Test and Brittle Fracture Initiation' *Ship Research Institute, Tokyo*, Paper No 25 (December, 1967)
11. 'Katalog zur Wahl der Stahlgütegruppen für geschweißte Stahlbauten', *Fachbuchreihe Schweißtechnik*, **26**, Deutcher Verlag für Schweißtechnik, Düsseldorf (1962)
12. KANFOR, S. S., *Korpusnaya Stal, Leningrad* (1960)
13. GRIFFITH, A. A., *Phil Trans, Royal Society*, **A-221**, 163–8 (1920)
14. 'Plain strain crack Toughness Testing of High Strength Metallic Materials', *ASTM Special Technical Publication No 410*
15. IRWIN, G. R., 'Fracture Dynamics' contribution to a Seminar held in Chicago, October, 1947; see 'Fracturing of Metals' published by ASM, Cleveland, Ohio (1948)
16. IRWIN, G. R., 'Crack Toughness Testing of Strain-rate sensitive Materials', *ASME Reprint 63-WA-217*, presented at Winter Annual Meeting, ASME, Philadelphia, Pa. (17–22 November, 1963)
17. OROWAN, E., *Trans. Inst. Eng. Shipbuilders in Scotland* (1945)
18. OROWAN, E., 'Fundamentals of Brittle Behaviour in Metals', *M.I.T. Symposium on Fatigue and Fracture of Metals*, 159, Wiley, New York (1950)
19. WELLS, A. A., 'Fracture Mechanics at and Beyond General Yield', *British Welding Journal*, **10**, No 11, 563 (1963)
20. BOYD, G. M., 'The Conditions for Unstable Rupturing of a Wide Plate', *Trans. Royal Instn. of Naval Architects*, **99**, 349–358 (1957)
21. VAN DEN BOOGART, A., and TURNER, C. E., 'Fracture Mechanics: A Review of Principles with special Reference to Applications for Glassy Plastics in Sheet Form', *J. Plastics Inst.* (August, 1963)
22. DOLBY, R. E., and BURDEKIN, F. M., 'Brittle Fracture in Perspective', *BWRA Bulletin*, **8** (May, June, July, 1967)
23. WILLIAMS, M. L., *ASTM Special Technical Publication No 158*, 11–41 (September, 1954)
24. Ship Structure Committee (USA), *Second Technical Progress Report* (1st July, 1950)
25. PUZAK, P. P., BABECKI, A. J., and PELLINI, W. S., *American Welding Journal*, 391S–401S (September, 1958)
26. HODGSON, J. and BOYD G. M., 'Brittle fracture in welded ships', *Trans. Royal Institution of Naval Architects*, **100**, 141–180 (1958)
27. Admiralty Advisory Committee on Structural Steel Report P2, HMSO (1960)
28. 'Practical Fracture Mechanics of Structural Steel', *Proc. Symp. Fracture Toughness Concepts for Weldable Structural Steel, UKAEA Risley, April, 1969*, UKAEA in association with Chapman & Hall

CHAPTER 7

RECOMMENDED PROCEDURES FOR THE SELECTION OF STEELS WITH REGARD TO NOTCH DUCTILITY

From the review given in Chapter 6, it will be seen that many methods have been proposed for assessing notch ductility requirements when selecting the correct type of steel to be used in a given structure.

Faced with a choice of these varied and sometimes conflicting procedures, the practical engineer is often at a loss to decide which system to use in an actual case.

This situation, however unsatisfactory, arises simply from the inherent difficulties of the problem and the incomplete state of knowledge. This is such that nobody is yet in a position to lay down precise rules covering the full range of engineering structures. However, the Navy Department Advisory Committee on Structural Steel has felt that some guidance can and should be given, and to this end two methods based on British practice are suggested as set out below. It should be noted that these apply to plate material and not to rolled sections. Although in the latter there are practical difficulties in obtaining impact values matching those of plate material, the aim should be to get as close as possible.

The first method is intended to apply to the general run of large fabricated structures, which are usually *not* stress relieved, such as ships' bridges, cranes, buildings etc., using carbon/manganese steels of up to about 25 ton/in² (40 kg/mm²) yield in thicknesses of up to about 1½ in (38 mm) or lower strength steels up to about 3 in (76 mm). This method is based on experience and provides results which accord fairly closely with established good practice for the types of structure quoted. However, it relies upon the allocation of somewhat arbitrary values to the various parameters, and it is clear that a far more scientifically based design procedure is desirable, which is why so many methods have been proposed, as reviewed in Chapter 6.

The second method also applies to carbon/manganese steels of up to about 25 ton/in² (40 kg/mm²) yield strength and is based upon results obtained by the Wells/BWRA Wide Plate Test (see Chapter 4). It is thus a procedure directed to the prevention of the initiation of brittle fracture. Method II exemplifies the present thinking of a body of qualified opinion in Great Britain, and in the form given in this Chapter, is already in use in the British oil and chemical industries for the design of pressure vessels, storage tanks and pipe systems.

Both methods give a guide to the Charpy V-notch properties required of the steel to enable a selection to be made from available steel specifications on the basis of the specified minimum Charpy impact properties.* The Charpy specimens are assumed to be cut with their axes parallel to the direction of rolling with the notch cut in a face which was originally perpendicular to the surface of the material. (Note: specimens cut in other directions will give very different values.)

A great variety of steels are available to the structural designer and an even greater variety of steel specifications. The principal categories of specifications are as follows:

1. British Standards Institution Specifications (BSS).
2. Foreign National Standard Specifications (e.g. DIN, ASTM).
3. Steelmakers Specifications for Proprietary Steels.
4. Steel Users Private Specifications.
5. The International Standards Organisation also plays an important role in the preparation of steel standards, but the main function of these is to facilitate rationalisation of National Standard Specifications.

In selecting material it is important to appreciate the distinction between a 'steel' and a 'specification'. A steel is the actual material supplied while a specification is a statement of the requirements with which the steel should comply. One type of steel, say 'Carbon Manganese Steel, Normalised', may satisfy many different specifications, while a single specification, say 'BS 4360 Grade 43 D' might be satisfied by several different types of steel. The two terms, however, are often used interchangeably.

For the reader's convenience, some of the more commonly used British Specifications are summarised in Table 7.1, indicating the yield stresses and notch ductility requirements, which are the main features of concern in the present context.

In selecting an appropriate steel for a given application, the designer will be principally concerned with minimum levels of (a) Yield strength, (b) Weldability and (c) Notch Ductility.

Guaranteed minimum yield strength values are included in the majority of modern specifications for structural and pressure vessel steels. Since the desired yield strength level will have been decided at an early stage of the

---

* As stated on page 59, it is impossible by means of simple formulae to convert the results obtained from any given test, using a given specimen, geometry or criterion, so as to correspond with the indications of any other test under different conditions, or with different specimens. Nevertheless, it is sometimes convenient to convert the UNITS. For example, foot-pounds can be converted directly to kilogramme-metres, using the appropriate factor. It is a practice in some quarters to report the results of impact tests in Kg.m/cm² (Kilogramme-metres per square centimetre). This value is obtained by dividing the actual readings in Kg.m by the nett cross-sectional area, in square centimetres, of the specimen at the notch. This area, of course, depends on the geometry of the specimen, so that to re-convert such values, in Kg.m/cm² to Kg.m it is necessary to know the type of specimen used in the tests.

Table 7.1. Summary of Steel Specifications

Note: This table is for guidance in selection only. The original specifications should be consulted in actual cases. The values given are for *PLATES*; the values for sections are, in general, different.

Table 7.1(a). BS.4360:1968, Weldable Structural Steels. (Figures in parentheses refer to footnotes.)

Grade	Yield stress (min) tonf/in² — up to and including ⅝ in	over ⅝ in up to and including 1½ in	over 1½ in up to and including 2½ in	Charpy V-notch ft lbf at Test Temperature Indicated — Room temp.	0°C	−5°C	−10°C	−15°C	−20°C	−30°C	−50°C	Normal Deoxidation Condition	Supply Condition(4)
40 A	—	—	—	20(2)	—	—	—	—	—	—	—	semi killed	as rolled
40 B	15·0	14·5	14·25	—	20	—	—	—	—	—	—	semi killed	as rolled
40 C	15·0	14·5(1)	14·25									semi killed	as rolled
40 D	17·0	16·0	15·5				30		20			semi killed with niobium	normalised
40 E	17·0	16·0	15·5						45	35	20	semi killed, fine grain	normalised
43 A	16·0	15·5(3)	15·0	20(2)	—	—	—	—	—	—	—	semi killed	as rolled
43 B	16·0	15·5(3)	15·0	—	20	—	—	—	—	—	—	semi killed	as rolled
43 C	16·0	15·5(3)	15·25				30		20			semi killed	as rolled
43 D	18·0	17·5	16·5				30		20	35		semi killed with niobium	normalised
43 E	18·0	17·5	16·5						45	35	20	semi killed, fine grain	normalised
50 A												semi killed	as rolled
50 B	23·0	22·5	22·0	—	—			20				semi killed with niobium	as rolled under ¾ in / normalised over ¾ in
50 C	23·0	22·5	22·0	—	—	30		20				semi killed with niobium	normalised
50 D	23·0	22·5	22·0						30	20		semi killed with niobium	normalised
55 C	29·0	28·0	27·0		20							semi killed with niobium	as rolled
55 E	29·0	28·0	27·0						45	35	20	fine grain	normalised

(For Grades 55 C and 55 E the yield-stress thickness ranges are: up to and including ⅝ in / over ⅝ in up to and including 1 in / over 1 in up to and including 1½ in.)

Notes:
1. Minimum yield stress 15 tonf/in² for material up to and including ¾ in thick.
2. Only if specified on the order.
3. Minimum yield stress 16 tonf/in² for material up to and including ¾ in thick.
4. Plates can be supplied in other conditions by agreement.

Table 7.1b. BS. 1501: 1964. Steels for Fired and Unfired Pressure Vessels

Grade	Yield Stress at Room Temperature tonf/in²			Charpy V-notch ft lbf at Temperatures Indicated					Steel Type	Normal Deoxidation Condition	Heat Treatment
	up to and including 5/8 in	over 5/8 in up to and including 1¼ in	over 1¼ in up to and including 2½ in	Room temp.	0° C	−15° C	−30° C	−50° C			
151–23 A	13·1	12·3	12·1	—	—	—	—	—	carbon	semi killed	normalised over 1¾ in thick
151–26 A	14·8	13·9	13·7	—	—	—	—	—			
151–28 A	16·0	15·0	14·8	—	—	—	—	—			
154–23	13·1			—	—	—	—	—	carbon	semi killed with aluminium	as rolled or normalised
154–26	14·8 up	to 3/8 in thick		—	—	—	—	—			
154–28	16·0			—	—	—	—	—			
161–23 A	13·1	12·3	12·1	—	—	—	—	—	carbon	silicon killed	normalised over 1¾ in thick
161–26 A	14·8	13·9	13·7	—	—	—	—	—			
161–28 A	16·0	15·0	14·8	—	—	—	—	—			
211–26 A	15·3	14·9	14·4	35	25				carbon-manganese	semi killed	normalised and stress relieved (over 1¾ in thick)
211–26 A	15·3	14·9	14·4	30	20						as rolled and stress relieved
211–28 A	16·5	16·0	15·5	35	25				carbon-manganese	semi killed	normalised and stress relieved (over 1¾ in thick)
211–28 A	16·5	16·0	15·5	30	20						as rolled and stress relieved
211–30 A	17·7	17·1	16·6	30	20				carbon-manganese	semi killed	normalised and stress relieved (over 1¾ in thick)
211–30 A	17·7	17·1	16·6	25	17						as rolled and stress relieved
211–32 A	18·8	18·4	17·7	30	20				carbon-manganese	semi killed	normalised and stress relieved (over 1¾ in thick)
211–32 A	18·8	18·4	17·7	25	17						as rolled and stress relieved
213–28 A	19·5	19·0	18·5	50	40	30	20		carbon-manganese	semi killed with niobium	normalised over 1¾ in
213–30 A	20·5	20·0	19·5	50	40	30	20				
213–32 A	22·0	21·5	21·0	50	40	30	20				
221–26 A	15·3	14·9	14·4	40	30	25			carbon-manganese	silicon killed	normalised and stress relieved (over 1¾ in thick)
221–26 A	15·3	14·9	14·4	35	25						as rolled and stress relieved
221–28 A	16·5	16·0	15·5	40	30	25					normalised and stress relieved (over 1¾ in thick)
221–28 A	16·5	16·0	15·5	35	25						as rolled and stress relieved
221–30 A	17·7	17·1	16·6	35	25						normalised and stress relieved (over 1¾ in thick)
221–30 A	17·7	17·1	16·6	30	20						as rolled and stress relieved
221–32 A	18·8	18·4	17·7	35	25						normalised and stress relieved (over 1¾ in thick)
221–32 A	18·8	18·4	17·7	30	20						as rolled and stress relieved
224–26 A	17·0	16·0	15·0	50	50	40	35	20	carbon-manganese	silicon killed with aluminium	normalised
224–28 A	18·5	17·5	16·5								
224–30 A	20·0	19·0	18·0								
224–32 A	21·0	20·0	19·0								

Table 7.1c. Navy Department Steels

Grade	Thickness	Tensile Strength Tonf/in²	Yield Stress (min) Tonf/in²	Charpy V-notch ft lbf at −30° C (min)	Deoxidation	Heat Treatment
A quality plate (Specification No DGS/5102B)	Up to and including 1 in	28–32	16	30 ft lb (crystallinity max. 75%)	Over 30 lb/ft² fully killed fine grain practice	Normalised
	Over 1 in up to and including 2 in	28–32	15			
B quality plate (Specification No DGS/5103A)	Up to and including 0·85 in	31–38	20	30 ft lb (crystallinity max. 75% up to 2 in)	Fully killed fine grain practice	Normalised
	Over 0·85 in up to and including 1·25 in	30–37	19			
	Over 1·25 in up to and including 3 in	29–36	18			

Table 7.1d. Lloyd's Ship Steels

(Lloyd's Register of Shipping Rules, 1970, Chapter P, Section 2)

Grade	Tensile Strength tonf/in²	Yield Stress tonf/in²	Charpy V-notch (ft lbf) at Temperature Indicated		Deoxidation	Heat Treatment
			0° C	−10° C		
A	26–32	not specified (assume 16 approx)	–	–	not rimmed	not specified
B	26–32		–	–	not rimmed	not specified
C	26–32		–	–	killed, fine grain	normalised over 1¼ in
D	26–32		35	–	not rimmed	not specified
E	26–32		–	45	killed, fine grain	normalised

Table 7.1e. Lloyd's Ship Steels—Higher Tensile

(Lloyd's Register of Shipping Rules, 1970, Chapter P, Section 3)

Grade	Test Temperature	Minimum Charpy V-notch energy	
		kgf.m	ft lbf
AH	0° C	2·765	20
DH	0° C	$\dfrac{4·84}{\sqrt{K^*}}$	$\dfrac{35}{\sqrt{K^*}}$
EH	−10° C	$\dfrac{6·22}{\sqrt{K^*}}$	$\dfrac{45}{\sqrt{K^*}}$

$*K = \dfrac{70·9}{Y+U}$ or $\dfrac{45}{Y+U}$ when Y and U are in kgf/mm² or tonf/in²
respectively
U = specified minimum tensile strength plus one half of the specified
   range
Y = specified minimum upper yield stress or 0·5% proof stress or
   0·7U, whichever is least
Lloyd's Rules do not give individual detailed specifications of higher
tensile ship steels, but require that full details of any proposed steel
be submitted for approval.
Lloyd's Rules for steel for boilers, pressure vessels and machinery
construction (Chapter Q of the Rules) are complex and cannot be
summarised.

design procedure, the designer may restrict his consideration to steel specifications providing the required level of strength.

There is a general relationship between weldability and strength in that an
increase in carbon and alloy content increases strength and has an adverse
effect on welding characteristics. However, better combinations of strength
and weldability can be obtained by reducing the carbon and increasing the
alloy content and certain specifications provide for exceptionally good welding characteristics at a given strength level. The welding characteristics are
controlled by restricting the carbon and alloy content to a specified maximum
value, based on an approximate carbon equivalent formula.

In the case of some plates, and virtually all sections which are supplied in
the as-rolled condition, the notch ductility improves with decreasing thickness. Thus a particular type of steel providing the desired V-notch Charpy
impact properties at ½ in (12 mm) thick may not be capable of achieving the
same level of notch ductility at 1 in (25 mm) or 1½ in (38 mm) thick. As in
general the requirement for notch ductility increases with increasing thickness,
it is frequently necessary to use a type of steel with inherently better notch
ductility for thick plates.

The important variable in the context of this book is the notch ductility
of the steel as indicated by the V-notch Charpy impact properties. Many
specifications now include guaranteed minima for the V-notch Charpy
energy absorption at one or more temperatures.

The approximate relationships between steel types are indicated in

Table 7.2. This Table is based on a scale of temperatures at which the indicated steel types would be expected to show about 20 ft lb (2·8 kg m) in the Charpy V-notch test. The Table, which should be regarded as informative rather than of direct applicability in the selection of specifications, is divided into three sections, according to approximate ranges of yield stress. However, while notch ductility must be taken into account in selecting the steel, it may not be necessary to order to a specification including a guaranteed minimum level. Where a steel specification does not include a requirement for impact testing, a general indication of the level of notch ductility can be obtained from this table and confirmed by an enquiry to the steel supplier.

Table 7.2a. Yield Stress about 15 ton/in²

Temperature for not less than 20 ft lb energy absorption in the V-notch Charpy impact test (°C)	Possible types of steel	Plate thickness (in)
20	Carbon steel—as rolled	1–1½
10	Carbon steel—as rolled	½–1
0	⎰ Carbon steel—as rolled	up to ½
	⎱ Carbon-manganese steel—as rolled	1–2
−10	⎰ Carbon-manganese steel—as rolled	below ½
	⎱ Carbon-manganese steel—normalised	up to 2
−30	Niobium-treated low carbon-manganese steel—normalised	up to 2
−50	Aluminium-treated carbon-manganese steel—normalised	up to 2

The Charpy V-notch impact properties assigned to the above steel types are those which can be normally expected. They do not necessarily conform to the values specified as minima in specifications (see Table 7.1).

Table 7.2b. Yield Stress about 20 ton/in²

Temperature for not less than 20 ft lb energy absorption in the V-notch Charpy impact test (°C)	Possible types of steel	Plate thickness (in)
over 20	Carbon steel—as rolled	1
0	⎧ Carbon steel—as rolled	up to ½
	⎨ Carbon-manganese steel—as rolled	
	⎩ or normalised	1 and above
−20	Carbon-manganese-niobium steel—controlled, rolled or normalised	up to 1
−30	Niobium-treated carbon-manganese steel—normalised	up to 1½
−50	Aluminium-treated carbon-manganese steel—normalised	up to 1½

Table 7.2c. Yield Stress about 25 ton/in²

Temperature for not less than 20 ft lb energy absorption in the V-notch Charpy impact test (°C)	Possible types of steel	Plate thickness (in)
0	Carbon-manganese-niobium steel— as rolled	up to ½
−30	⎧ Special controlled rolled steel ⎨ Special grain controlled normalised ⎩ steel	up to 1 up to 1½
−40	Grain controlled carbon-manganese steel—quenched and tempered	up to 1½

7.1. METHOD I

7.1.1. General Principles

It has become common practice to specify the notch ductility required of a steel by means of the Charpy V-notch test, by requiring that a specified energy value shall be attained at a specified temperature. This is, of course an over-simplification, as can be seen from other Chapters of this book, but it is widely used and fairly well established by experience for the general run of engineering steel structures. Other, more sophisticated criteria are necessary in special circumstances, particularly those involving very low temperature (say below −20° C) or large thickness (say over 3 in).

It must be emphasised that Method I is not valid for service temperatures below about −20° C.

To apply the method, the designer must be in possession of reasonably full information relating to the following factors:

1. The strength level and general type of steel to be employed.
2. The details of the design, including plate thickness, size of section and the types of welded joints.
3. The conditions under which fabrication will be carried out and the procedure to be employed.
4. The conditions of loading and the temperatures to which the structure will be subjected in service.
5. Any exceptional circumstances which would dictate a need for extra security against the risk of catastrophic brittle fracture.

7.1.2. Procedure

The first step in the procedure is to determine the lowest temperature likely to be encountered in normal service, referred to here as the 'minimum design service temperature'. For this purpose the minimum design service temperature is defined as the lowest one day mean ambient temperature plus 10° C, (see Fig. 7.1) or, where relevant, the minimum metal temperature if this is known (i.e. that of a vessel's contents), whichever is the lower. This temperature is then adjusted by adding or subtracting increments of

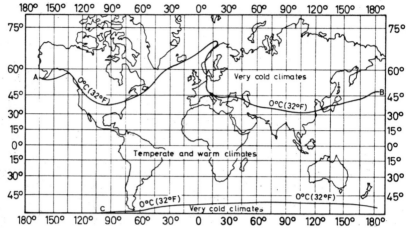

Fig. 7.1. *Map of world showing isotherms. The line A–B corresponds to the (0°C, 32°F) January isotherm and the line C–D to the (0°C, 32°F) July isotherm as given on the Philips world relations temperature chart*

temperature, as detailed later, to take account of various relevant design conditions.

Based on experience of large 'field' structures such as welded ships, bridges, storage tanks, etc., fabricated of mild steel and operating at ambient temperatures in temperate regions, i.e. down to about −10° C, it has been found that the probability of brittle fracture may be regarded as acceptably low for mild steel plates up to about ¾ in (20 mm) thick. Such steel characteristically gives an energy absorption of about 20 ft lb (2·8 kg m) in a V-notch Charpy impact test carried out at +20° C, i.e. 30° C above the minimum design service temperature.

7.1.2.1. *Temperature*

The first adjustment is, then, the addition of 30° C to the minimum design service temperature.

7.1.2.2. *Thickness*

Thickness has a profound effect on the liability to brittle fracture. This effect is partly geometrical and partly metallurgical, as discussed in other chapters. It is therefore prudent to require a higher level of notch ductility in thicker materials. Adjustments to the temperature should be applied as shown in Table 7.3.

7.1.2.3. *Stress Level*

The nominal design tensile stress in a structure is an important consideration since high design stress increases the elastic energy which is stored in the structure and which would be released in the event of a fracture. Moreover the higher the stress, the smaller the defect that may develop into a fracture.

Table 7.3

	For steels of yield strength up to about 25 ton/in²					For steels of yield strength of 16 ton/in² and less.	
Thickness (in)	$\frac{1}{2}$	$\frac{3}{4}$	1	$1\frac{1}{4}$	$1\frac{1}{2}$	2	3
Thickness (mm)	13	19	25	32	38	51	76
Adjustment:	$+10°$ C	$0°$ C	$-10°$ C	$-15°$ C	$-20°$ C	$-25°$ C	$-30°$ C

The adjustments for intermediate thicknesses can be obtained by interpolation.

It is prudent therefore to provide additional notch ductility in highly stressed structures, and the following adjustments to the temperature are suggested (Table 7.4).

Table 7.4

Maximum Design Stress	Adjustment
10 ton/in² (16 kg/mm²)	$-10°$ C
15 ton/in² (24 kg/mm²)	$-15°$ C

Pro-rata adjustments can be made for other stress levels.

Note: When the stresses are always compressive, there is normally no need for notch ductility control.

7.1.2.4. *Quality of Design and Fabrication*

If special care is exercised in design so as to reduce stress concentrations and other undesirable design features (see Chapter 5) some slight relaxation in notch ductility may be justified provided that a high standard of workmanship and inspection is assured. In such cases it is suggested that an allowance of $+10°$ C may be made.

7.1.2.5. *Required Safety Level*

Where failure of the structure would have serious consequences, particularly where loss of life might occur, it is to be expected that special care will be taken in design, fabrication and inspection (see Section 7.1.2.4 above), but a still greater margin of safety might be desirable. It is suggested that in such cases, a further adjustment of $-10°$ C, or in extreme cases $-20°$ C, be provided.

Note: The method should *not* be considered as an adequate guide to the design of nuclear reactor pressure vessels or other critical applications, for which special test procedures must be used.

7.1.2.6. *Type of Loading*

Departure from static loading can increase the liability to brittle fracture. Firstly, cyclic or intermittent loads may give rise to fatigue cracking, thus providing a defect from which low stress fractures could initiate. Secondly, rapid application of loading (shock or impact) can produce high stresses for periods long enough to initiate brittle fractures from potential sources such as cracks or defects which might otherwise be innocuous.

To afford some measure of protection against these the following adjustments to the temperature are suggested (Table 7.5).

Table 7.5

Cyclic or intermittent loads	$-10°$ C
Shock impact loads	$-20°$ C

7.1.2.7. *Thermal Stress Relief*

Thermal stress relief can considerably reduce the liability of a structure to the initiation of a low stress fracture, and is therefore recommended where practicable. However, for most of the structures to which Method I is applicable, thermal stress relief is not practicable for reasons of size. Moreover, in many cases the cost of such treatment would not be justified.

To be effective, thermal stress relief must be carried out in such a manner as fully to relieve the residual stresses and also to rectify local embrittlement resulting from fabrication processes. Expert advice should be sought on the appropriate heat treatment for a particular steel and application. Because of the difficulty of guaranteeing that a stress relieving treatment has been fully effective, it is possible that some risk of brittle fracture remains. For this reason it is proposed to limit the allowance to be applied for post heat treated weldments to an increase in temperature not exceeding $30°$ C.

7.1.3. Summary

These various adjustments are summarised below for easy reference, but the warnings given should always be borne in mind (see also Notes on pages 112ff).

1. *Design Temperature*

Min. design service temp. (°C)	-20	-10	±0	$+10$	$+20$
Datum temperature (°C) (subject to adjustments as below)	$+10$	$+20$	$+30$	$+40$	$+50$

2. *Thickness*

	For steels of yield strength up to about 25 ton/in²					For steels of yield strength of 16 ton/in² or less	
Max. thickness (in)	$\frac{1}{2}$	$\frac{3}{4}$	1	$1\frac{1}{4}$	$1\frac{1}{2}$	2	3
Max. thickness (mm)	13	19	25	32	38	51	76
Adjustment:	$+10°$C	$0°$C	$-10°$C	$-15°$C	$-20°$C	$-25°$ C	$-30°$ C

3. *Stress Level*

Design maximum stress (ton/in²)	10	15
Design maximum stress (kg/mm²)	16	24
Adjustment	$-10°$C	$-15°$C

4. *Type of Loading*

Type of Loading	Adjustment
Cyclic or intermittent	$-10°$ C
Shock	$-20°$ C

5. *Quality of Design and Fabrication*

Rating	Normal	Special Care
Adjustment:	0° C	$+10°$ C

6. *Safety Level*

Rating	Normal	Extra	Special
Adjustment	0° C	$-10°$ C	$-20°$ C

7. *Thermal Stress Relief*

Thermal Stress Relief	None	Fully Effective
Adjustment:	0° C	$+30°$ C

7.1.4. Charpy Energy Values

Having obtained the temperature adjusted as above, a corresponding Charpy V-notch energy level is selected from the table below, in which energy is related to the yield point of the steel to be used:

Yield Stress		Energy	
(ton/in²)	(kg/mm²)	(ft lb)	(kg.m)
Up to 16	25	20	2·8
over 16–20	25–32	25	3·5
over 20–23	32–36	30	4·2
over 23–25	36–40	35	4·9

The temperature and associated energy thus determined are then plotted on the diagram in Fig. 7.2. In this diagram the Charpy V-notch requirements

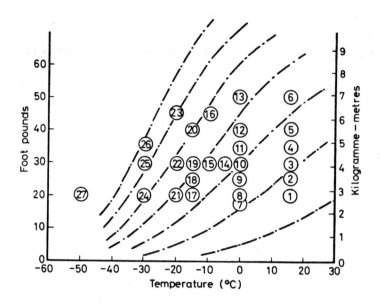

Fig. 7.2. *Energy-temperature diagram*

Table 7.6

Point No.	B.S.4360	B.S.1501	Lloyd's	Min. Def. (Navy)	Other specs.
1	40B, 43B				
2		211–30A†, 211–32A†			
3		211–26A†, 28A†, 30A*, 32A*; 221–30A†, 32A†			
4		211–26A*, 28A*; 221–26A†, 28A†, 30A*, 32A*			
5		221–26A*, 28A*			
6		224–26A, 28A, 30A, 32A; 213–28A, 30A, 32A			
7		211–30A†, 32A†			
8	40C, 43C, 55C	211–26A†, 28A†, 30A*, 32A*; 221–30A†, 32A†			
9		211–26A*, 28A*; 221–26A†, 28A†, 30A*, 32A*			
10		221–26A*, 28A*			
11			D		
12		213–28A, 30A, 32A			
13		224–26A, 28A, 30A, 32A			
14	50C	213–28A, 30A, 32A			
15	40D, 43D				
16			E		
17	50C				
18		221–26A*, 28A*			
19		213–28A, 30A, 32A			
20		224–26A, 28A, 30A, 32A			
21	40D, 43D				
22	50D				
23	40E, 43E, 55E				
24	50D	213–28A, 30A, 32A			
25				A & B	
26	40E, 43E, 55E	224–26A, 28A, 30A, 32A			
27	40E, 43E, 55E	224–26A, 28A, 30A, 32A			

* = Normalised and stress relieved   † = As rolled and stress relieved
For further particulars of specifications cited, see Table 7.1

in relevant British steel specifications are shown as numbered circles. The specifications corresponding to these numbered points can be identified by means of Table 7.6. By following the guide curves from the temperature/energy point determined by the method, one can select standard steels which will meet the requirements of the case under study. For example, if by using the method it were found that $T = 10°$ C and $E = 20$ ft lb, it would be found from the diagram that the steels corresponding to the numbered points above and to the left of the guide curve through this point would comply, e.g. points 3, 7 and 8.

7.1.5. Examples

Example 1. The main girders for a building are to be made up from steel having a yield point of 22 ton/in^2 with flanges of $1\frac{1}{2}$ in thickness. Design stress is 12 ton/in^2 and a minimum temperature reached by the framework is 0° C. The adjusted temperature for plotting in Fig. 7.2 is found as in the Table below.

For steel with a yield stress of 22 ton/in^2 the appropriate energy level is 30 ft lb (from table in Section 7.1.4).

	Temperature Increment (for no stress relief)
1. Adjusted minimum design service temperature 0 + 30	+30
2. Thickness $1\frac{1}{2}$ in	−20
3. Stress level 12 ton/in^2 (interpolated)	−12
4. Type of load, static	0
5. Quality of design and fabrication, normal	0
6. Required safety level, normal	0
Resultant temperature T° C	−2

Thus, in the absence of thermal stress relief it will be necessary to require 30 ft lb at −2° C. By reference to Fig. 7.2, it is found that steels corresponding to points numbered 6, 10, 11, 14 and 17 would comply closely. These include several of the B.S. 4360 and B.S. 1501 grades, and also Lloyd's Grade D. A choice can be made among these specifications on the basis of yield stress (by reference to Table 7.1) and economics. It would probably be found that B.S. 4360, Grade 50C would be the most suitable.

This requirement is consistent with that for structural steel in building to B.S. 449.

If the particular region of the structure were such that a single failure would result in complete collapse, it would be necessary to subtract 10° C in the temperature determination under heading 6, Safety Level. If this were the case the requirement would become 30 ft lb at −12°C, and to meet this B.S. 4360 grade 50 D would be found suitable.

Example 2. The crane girders for a steel teeming bay are to be made in a steel of 14–16 ton/in² yield strength with a design working stress of 8 ton/in² (from fatigue considerations). The ambient temperature will not fall below +10° C when the crane is working. The thickness of the tension flange varies from 1 in to 3 in.

	Thickness (inches)			
	1	1½	2	3
1. Adjusted Temperature (10 + 30)	+40	+40	+40	+40
2. Thickness	−10	−20	−25	−30
3. Fluctuating load	−10	−10	−10	−10
4. Stress level 8 ton/in²	−8	−8	−8	−8
5. Quality of design and fabrication, special care	+10	+10	+10	+10
6. Safety level, extra	−10	−10	−10	−10
7. Thermal stress relief, none	0	0	0	0
Resultant temperature T° C	+12	+2	−3	−8

Energy corresponding to 16 ton/in² yield strength = 20 ft lb.

It will be seen by reference to Fig. 7.2 that there are several steels from which selection can be made, lying to left of the guide lines through these points, which would be suitable as regards notch toughness, although some of these might be eliminated by other considerations.

7.2. METHOD II

This method is based upon results obtained from Wells/BWRA wide plate tests, which test is discussed in Chapter 4.

This wide plate test provides a reliable method for estimating service performance in so far as the *initiation* of low stress fracture under static loading is concerned. The criterion used is the temperature at which the test specimen develops a mean strain of at least 0·5% before fracture. Such a strain exceeds by a considerable margin that corresponding to the mean membrane stress in storage tanks, pressure vessels, etc., but strains of this order can occur around large openings, such as manways, for example during hydrostatic testing for the first time. There is evidence that the results of the wide plate test are not much affected by the actual value of the plastic strain reached in general yielding of the specimen. Other factors such as the notch depth, and the weld metal properties in relation to those of the steel under test have a much more marked effect on the results. The data derived from the test is now used extensively, especially in the oil and chemical industries for the selection of steels for pressure vessels, storage tanks and pipe systems, and is also gradually being extended to other types of structures. As yet there is insufficient test data to cover a very wide range of materials, but a substantial number of tests have been completed on carbon manganese steels, and these results have been subjected to critical appraisal.

Based on such wide plate test data as is available, the curves in Figs. 7.3 (as welded) and 7.4 (stressed relieved) are considered to represent the minimum service temperatures at which plates of the indicated thicknesses and specifications can safely be used.

It will be seen that for the 'as welded' condition (Fig. 7.3) the minimum design service temperature which can be recommended is very low for thin steels but for the thick plates, it is in the range of normal atmospheric temperatures. The maximum thickness at present permitted for pressure vessel construction without stress relief is $1\frac{1}{2}$ in (38 mm), i.e. the limit indicated in Fig. 7.3.

Wells wide-plate tests on specimens thermally stress-relieved after welding show very considerable improvement in performance compared with 'as welded' specimens, the 'failure temperature' (in the test) being lowered by some

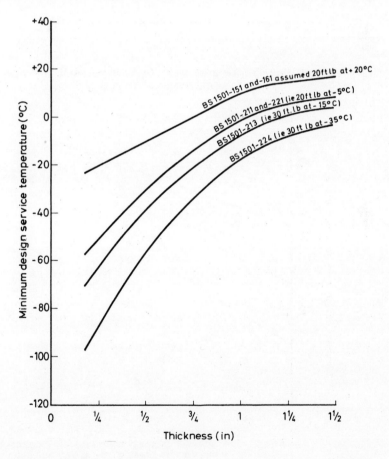

Fig. 7.3. *Minimum design service temperature thickness relationship for as welded fabrications*

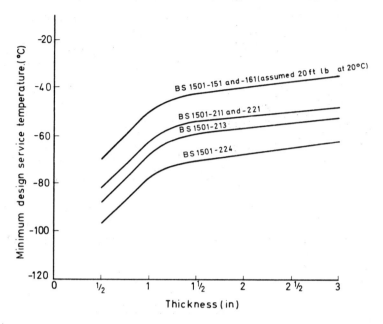

Fig. 7.4. *Minimum design service temperature: Thickness relationship for stress relieved fabrications*

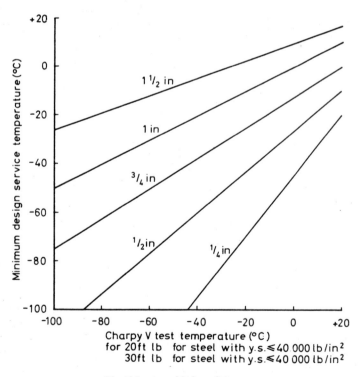

Fig. 7.5. *As welded condition*

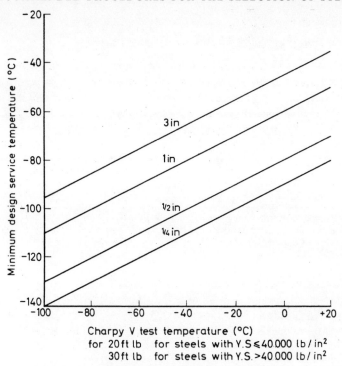

Fig. 7.6. *Stress relieved condition*

70 deg. C and this is reflected in Fig. 7.4. This can to some extent be attributed to the reduction of residual stress, but mainly to the repair of metallurgical damage (strain ageing) caused by the welding process. These effects are becoming recognised as the most important factor in assessing the notch ductility of weldments required to be used in the 'as welded' condition.

It has been found that an arithmetical relationship exists between Charpy V impact values and the results of the wide plate tests for carbon and carbon manganese steels[1] and this relationship has been used to derive Figs. 7.5 and 7.6. By means of these diagrams it is possible to determine the temperature at which certain Charpy V energy values (i.e. 20 ft lb (2·8 kg m) for steel up to about 40 000 lb/in^2 (275 N/mm^2) yield strength and 30 ft lb (4·2 kg m) for stronger steels), are required for various temperature-thickness relationships.

The minimum design service temperatures for the as welded condition in Fig. 7.5 where cracks can be initiated from metallurgically damaged weld defects, is considered to represent the most severe condition for crack initiation. In the stress relieved case, i.e. in the absence of metallurgically damaged zones, the curves given in Fig. 7.6 can be considered to represent the minimum design service temperatures for plates containing a defect size corresponding to that of the relatively small artificial defects in the wide plate test specimens. Working near to the limits given in Fig. 7.6 therefore presupposes that a reasonable standard of workmanship and inspection has been employed.

7.2.1. Examples

Some examples of applying Method II are given below:

Example 1. An 80 ft dia × 60 ft high oil storage tank with shell plate thicknesses ranging from $\frac{1}{2}$–$\frac{3}{4}$ in and a design stress necessitating material of 15 ton/in² yield strength. The tank operates in a rather cold climate and is designed for a minimum design service temperature of $-10°$ C.

No stress relief will be used and therefore Fig. 7.5 applies:

	Thickness (inches)		
	$\frac{1}{4}$	$\frac{1}{2}$	$\frac{3}{4}$
Charpy test temperature (derived from Fig. 7.5 by reading at a service temperature of $-10°$ C) Energy required (YP under 40 000 lb/in²)	$>+20°$ C 20 ft lb	$+20°$ C 20 ft lb	$0°$ C 20 ft lb

By a similar procedure to that used in Method I and by applying Fig. 7.2 it is seen that a suitable steel quality for the $\frac{1}{4}$ in and $\frac{1}{2}$ in thick plate would be B.S. 4360:1968 Grade 43B. The notch ductility requirements for the $\frac{3}{4}$ in material would be met by B.S. 4360:1968 Grade 43C (20 ft lb at $0°$ C, yield point 15·5 ton/in²).

Example 2. A pressure vessel fabricated in $1\frac{1}{2}$ in thick carbon/manganese steel with a design stress necessitating a material with a yield strength of 45 000 lb/in² and a minimum design service temperature of $-15°$ C. Since the yield strength is in excess of 40 000 lb/in² the Charpy V temperature for 30 ft lb is required. From Fig. 7.5 a steel with a Charpy value of 30 ft lb at $-50°$ C would be needed if the vessel is operated in the 'as welded' condition.

If however, the vessel were to be thermally stress relieved, Fig. 7.6 would apply and it is seen that from the point of view of brittle fracture any carbon/manganese steel would suffice, and no impact requirement would need to be stated.

7.3. NOTES ON THE FOREGOING STEEL SELECTION PROCEDURES

7.3.1. High Strain Rates

When steels are subject to loading at high strain rates the use of the Wells-BWRA wide plate test in its normal form is not appropriate, neither can this test be relied upon to determine with accuracy the resistance of a steel to fracture propagation. Method II must not therefore be used for Selection of materials for such service conditions.

7.3.2. Steels with Unspecified Impact Properties

When Charpy values are not specified, values must either be assumed or obtained by tests, e.g. for B.S. 4360 Grade 43A, a Charpy value of 20 ft lb

(2·8 kg m) at $+20°$ C for plates between $\frac{3}{4}$ in (19 mm) and $1\frac{1}{4}$ in (32 mm) thick might be assumed, although this specification has no impact test requirements.

7.3.3. Notch Ductility Requirement for Weld Metals

Low stress fractures almost invariably initiate at welds and associated heat affected zones although the fracture itself almost always propagates in the parent plate, away from the line of the weld. Few investigations have been made into the notch ductility requirements for weld metal and for this reason it is generally considered good practice to require weld metal to possess the same level of Charpy energy as that specified for the base material. However, recent work has shown that the notch ductility required in any part of a welded zone should be related to its tensile strength, so that if weld metal of a higher strength than the parent metal is used, a higher Charpy V energy will be required than that of the parent metal.

In the case of manual electrodes used for welding mild steel, or for fine grained steel intended for service at temperatures down to about $-20°$ C or $-30°$ C these requirements present little difficulty. The weld metal deposited by most good quality rutile-based mild steel welding electrodes will meet, at least when welding is done in the down-hand position, the requirements of B.S. 639 Grade 3 which specifies a minimum Charpy energy of 45 ft lb (7·1 kg m) at $-10°$ C. Usually a higher notch ductility can be obtained with basic lime–fluoride (low hydrogen) electrodes. Weld metal deposited by automatic processes such as submerged arc (Ref B.S. 4165) or electroslag welding may not always achieve a similar level of notch ductility to that prevailing in the plate material. In such cases it may be considered that the relative freedom of the weld metal from such defects as slag inclusion allows some relaxation. Initiation of fracture is usually due to the presence of a physical defect such as lack of fusion or crack. Defects of this nature are usually minimised by machine welding.

More precise recommendations for notch ductility of weld metal than those given above cannot be made in the present state of knowledge. Initiation of low stress brittle fracture in weld metal is now being studied by such refined methods as the crack opening displacement test, which has only recently been developed. From the small amount of data so far collected there appears to be no evidence that the notch ductility of weld metal can with safety be permitted to be less than that required for parent plate of equivalent strength and thickness. However, the difference in strengths of weld metal and plates, the shape of the weld nugget and its heat affected zone may all influence the performance of the composite weldment. Much more work is required to elucidate these factors.

7.3.4. Limitations of Methods

Method I should not be applied to structures involving temperatures below $-20°$ C and Method II should not be used below $-100°$ C. For service at temperatures below these limits it is recommended that the steel selection be based on a specific test programme involving type tests, for example Wells-BWRA Wide Plate, Robertson or Drop Weight Tear Tests, depending on the structural applications. If for certain applications it may be deemed necessary to provide for the arrest of a running fracture, however initiated, tests such as the Robertson Crack Arrest and the Pellini Drop Weight Tear test should be used to verify that the isothermal transition temperature of the proposed steel is at or below the service temperature. The results of such tests may be associated, by correlation, with Charpy V tests for the purpose of quality control (see Chapter 6).

In conclusion it must be emphasised that methods for the selection of steel qualities are subject to continuous evolution and refinement. No single method has yet been devised which permits this selection to be made in precise terms. For this reason the above procedures can only be regarded as aids to judgement. This judgement, in the last resort, is the responsibility of the designer and must be formed in the light of all the relevant circumstances of each case.

Reference

1. COTTON, H. C., 'Structural Steel for Containers', *ISI/BISRA Joint Conference on Strong Tough Steels, Scarborough* (4–6 April, 1967)

'GOLDEN RULES' FOR THE AVOIDANCE
OF BRITTLE FRACTURE

The following 'Rules' have been compiled in concise form for ready reference. They should not be regarded as a substitute for a fuller understanding of the problem, which can only be obtained from further study. Although the 'Rules' are classified under Design, Materials Selection and Fabrication, they are all of particular concern to designers, and to managements.

GENERAL

Good communications and collaboration between all departments: designers, suppliers, fabricators and erectors are essential. Many failures have resulted from deficiencies in this aspect.

Before putting work in hand, check all stages of the design and specifications. In cases of doubt seek expert advice. Most failures are caused by errors or omissions.

DESIGN

1. Ascertain the relevant facts about the intended service of the structures, and particularly the lowest temperatures likely to be encountered, the character of the loading, i.e. whether static, fluctuating, intermittent, impact etc.

2. Choose the sections and thicknesses so as to avoid abrupt changes in section and to keep thicknesses to a minimum. Remember that increasing the thickness increases the brittle fracture hazard.

3. Take special care in the design of details and connections to minimise stress concentrations and to ensure easy welding and inspection. Avoid multiple thicknesses where possible and pay special attention to minor fittings attached to main strength members.

4. Wherever possible, locate welds clear of stress concentrations and avoid placing several welds close together, particularly fillet welds.

5. Specify welding procedures and quality control checks, such as will ensure that the designer's intentions are fulfilled.

MATERIAL SELECTION

6. Remember that the judicious choice of steel, and its correct specification is a prime duty of the designer and an overriding factor in controlling the risk of brittle fracture.

7. Decide the tensile properties of the steel to be used, remembering that high tensile steel requires a higher margin of notch ductility and greater care in fabrication and welding (see Chapter 5). Do not ask for a higher strength than necessary.

8. Consider whether 'stress relief' heat treatment of the finished structure is feasible, remembering that such treatment is very beneficial, when properly done. The choice of steel requirements will be influenced by this decision (see Chapter 7).

9. Consider whether pre-loading or proof loading is feasible and expedient, bearing in mind the considerations given in Chapter 5. This also will influence the choice of steel requirements.

10. Decide the notch ductility required (see Chapters 5, 6 and 7).

11. Select a standard steel specification which embodies the requirements. If no suitable standard is available make, in consultation with the steelmakers, your own specification or amend an existing one.

12. Remember that some fabrication processes may adversely affect the notch ductility of the steel.

13. Ascertain what 'type tests' (see Chapter 4) have been made on the proposed steel, so that you know as much as possible about its properties and behaviour.

14. Ascertain from the steelmakers any special precautions required in the fabrication, welding and heat treatment of the proposed steel.

NOTE: IF FOR PRACTICAL REASONS YOU HAVE TO USE A STEEL THAT DOES NOT FULLY MEET THE NOTCH DUCTILITY REQUIREMENTS THE RULES RELATING TO DESIGN AND FABRICATION BECOME ALL THE MORE IMPORTANT.

FABRICATION

15. Remember that the care put into the design and choice of material can be nullified by apparently minor faults or carelessness in fabrication and welding. The quality of the welding has a very important bearing on the safety of the structure. Non-load bearing attachments and 'minor' details require the same standard of workmanship as the main structure to which they are attached.

16. Choose a weld metal having a level of notch ductility appropriate to the steel and application of the structure.

17. Make sure that the standard of inspection matches the care taken in other aspects of the job. An undetected but significant fault may spell failure.

Pay particular attention to the assessment of flaws and to their correction when necessary. Repair welds should be meticulously inspected.

18. Avoid uncontrolled tack welds, arc strikes and minor temporary attachments. (Particularly on high tensile steel.) Prefer clamping to welding for such attachments.

REMEMBER THAT IN THE LAST RESORT, THE SAFETY OF THE STRUCTURE DEPENDS MOSTLY ON YOUR JUDGEMENT, AND ON THE IMPLEMENTATION OF THE DESIGN REQUIREMENTS.

INDEX